APRS

Tracks, Maps and Mobiles

A Guide to the

Automatic
Position
Reporting
System

By Stan Horzepa,
WA1LOU

Published by:

ARRL

225 Main Street
Newington, CT
06111-1494 USA

ARRLWeb: http://www.arrl.org/

CONTENTS

FOREWORD

APRS is not so much a revolution in packet radio as it is more of a return to basics in Amateur Radio communications. Back in 1978 when digital communications was first authorized in the USA, the ability to effectively communicate live among a group of other digital stations was soon lost with the advent of the Bulletin Boards. While the non-real-time nature of the BBS was an advantage to routine exchange of message traffic, and was the forbear of the ubiquitous human condition of "you've got mail," it perpetuated the legacy of point-to-point style communications used on phone lines and took no advantage of the point-to-multipoint capabilities of radio.

Always trying to find a way to use the accuracy and speed of packet to special events and field activities, I wrote the *Connectionless Emergency Traffic System (CETS)* in 1984 for exchanging messages, triage and patient information among dozens of hospitals in support of the National Disaster Medical System exercises. Written for the Commodore C-64, it was upgraded to a PC. Maps were added in 1988. By 1992, the plummeting prices for automatic position determination of GPS combined with my one and only call-sign suffix gave birth to APRS.

The first few years of APRS had many hurdles to overcome due to the legacy of point-to-point packet radio and BBSs whose requirements were exclusive to APRS digipeating. Over the years, the digipeaters of the 1980s had all been converted to nodes and digipeating was forcefully discouraged. But the growth of public e-mail was rapidly depleting interest in packet radio. With the rise of the Web in 1994 and phone line modems going to 14.4 and higher data rates, the time was ripe for something new for packet radio.

In this time frame, the growth of APRS from zero to over 600 dedicated APRS digipeaters in the USA has been phenomenal. Even the final months of the space station *MIR*'s packet system was given over to APRS-style communications. Several Space Shuttle APRS experiments were conducted, leading to permission to use the three 1200-baud PACSATs in orbit for APRS digipeating in 1999. This infrastructure, along with the worldwide Internet linked system, *APRServe*, makes APRS an important aspect of Amateur Radio for the new millenium.

My only caution is that we remain focused on the original intent and design of APRS to provide tactical, real-time digital communications. We must remain vigilant that compromises to satisfy the 99% of the time that APRS is on the air for routine operations in benign conditions over large areas do not impact its capabilities for short-range, rapid and accurate delivery of information under stress.

Welcome to APRS. I'll see you on the map!

Bob Bruninga, WB4APR
December 1999

ACKNOWLEDGMENTS

I wish to thank the APRS software authors for their invaluable assistance throughout this project. They answered all my questions quickly and without a whimper. So, thank you, Bob Bruninga (WB4APR), Steve Dimse (K4HG), Brent Hildebrand (KH2Z), Mike Musick (NØQBF), Keith Sproul (WU2Z), Mark Sproul (KB2ICI), and Rob Wittner (KZ5RW).

Also, I wish to thank my editor, Joel Kleinman (N1BKE).

Finally, I wish to thank my wife, Laurie, and daughter, Hayley, whose patience throughout this project helped make it a reality.

DEDICATION

To my faithful canine companion, Q-T Pie, who laid at my feet, keeping them warm, while I sat at the computer hacking away at this book.

ABOUT THE AUTHOR

So you won't think that this book was written by some bozo who just got off the bus at 225 Main Street, here is a list of my qualifications:

- Red Sox fan since 1958 (knows how to work under stress)
- Amateur Radio operator since 1969 (knows a thing or tube about radio)
- *QST* and ARRL author since 1977 (lots of practice writing right)
- Computer owner and operator since 1978 (remembers paying $599 for 8k of RAM)
- Technical writer since 1979 (still more practice writing right)
- Packet radio operator since 1984 (remembers when there were only four active stations in all of Connecticut)
- APRS operator since 1994 (remembers when there were only four active stations in all of Connecticut)
- Father of teenaged girl since 1998 (fondly recalls the good old days when there was only Red Sox stress)

To learn even more about "The Author," brush the cobwebs off my Web site at **http://www.tapr.org/~wa1lou**. You can also keyboard at me via my APRS digipeater (WA1LOU-15), which is strategically located on one of the highest peaks in the county ("T'ain't nothing higher south of here 'til you hit Venezuela!") Or you can email me at **wa1lou@arrl.net**.

1

INTRODUCTION

APRS is the acronym for *Automatic Position Reporting System.** Invented by Bob Bruninga, WB4APR, it integrates hardware and software to permit Amateur Radio operators to disseminate data concerning real-time events quickly, and to graphically represent that data on maps displayed on their computers.

The system uses packet radio as the means of disseminating the data. Unlike traditional packet operations in which communications occurs on a one-to-one basis, however, APRS uses unconnected packets to disseminate data on a one-to-all basis.

An APRS packet may contain station location (latitude and longitude) and station type (homes, portables, mobiles, digipeaters, weather stations, etc) information. An APRS station receiving these packets, processes the information contained therein, and displays an appropriate symbol on a map showing the location of the station. If a station such as a mobile or portable station is in motion, APRS changes the position of that station on the map when it receives a new position packet that indicates a change of location.

The station in motion may be a radio, TNC and laptop computer running APRS. As that station travels along its route, the station operator updates the position of the station on the APRS map and APRS relays the new position to other APRS stations to update the position of the station on their APRS maps.

On the other hand, the station in motion may be a radio, TNC and a Global Positioning System (GPS) receiver, which receives signals from Earth-orbiting satellites to calculate

*APRS is a registered trademark of APRS Engineering LLC, which reserves all rights to its use for commercial products.

its location. The GPS receiver periodically sends position information to the TNC of the station in motion, which relays it to other APRS stations in order to update the position of the moving station on their APRS maps.

Place an APRS station in an emergency vehicle being used in a disaster area or in the lead car of a parade, and the possibility of using APRS as a public service tool for tactical communications becomes obvious.

In addition to tracking stations in motion, APRS also tracks any object in motion when the position of that object is entered into the system. For example, you can enter the latitude and longitude of a hurricane and the position of the hurricane appears on the map of everyone using APRS on that channel. In that weather vein, you can also interface weather-monitoring equipment to an APRS station to disseminate real-time weather information to other APRS stations.

As with traditional packet radio stations, APRS stations use digipeaters to propagate their transmissions, but unlike traditional packet, APRS stations do not have to specify a digipeater path. Rather, APRS stations can use generic digipeater paths so that no prior knowledge of the network is needed. To further propagate APRS, the Internet is an integral part of the system and is used for collecting and disseminating current APRS data on an international and real-time basis.

THE PURPOSE OF THIS BOOK

This book describes how to install, configure, and use the hardware and software components of APRS.

This book covers the following versions of APRS:
• *APRS (DOS)*, the DOS version.
• *MacAPRS*, the Macintosh version
• *WinAPRS*, a Windows version
• *APRS+SA*, a Windows version that uses Delorme Street Atlas maps
• *pocketAPRS*, the 3Com Palm III Connected Organizer version
• *TH-D7*, the APRS software built into Kenwood's TH-D7 transceiver

CONVENTIONS USED IN THIS BOOK

This book uses the following conventions:

Bold indicates information that you type at a keyboard (for example, "type **CD APRS** and press **Enter**") or selections you make in software (for example, "select **Quit** from the File menu" or "click on the **OK** button").

Bold also highlights Internet URLs and email addresses (for example,

http://www.tapr.org/~kh2z/aprsplus/ and

bruninga@nadn.navy.mil).

Italics indicate file names, path names, directories, book titles and variable information. For example, in the file name *aprs###.zip*, *###* is the variable information.

Bold italics indicate variable information that you type at a keyboard. For example, in "type *c:\pkunzip -d a:\aprs###*," the software version number (*###*) is the variable portion of the information you type at a keyboard.

2

HARDWARE INSTALLATION

T his chapter describes the equipment you need for APRS and how to connect that equipment in your APRS station. APRS with and without a GPS receiver are the most common APRS configurations and those are the configurations of equipment described here.

BASIC COMPONENTS

A basic APRS station consists of radio equipment, terminal node controller (TNC) and some means of providing the station's position to the TNC for transmission by the radio.

In a typical home base APRS station, the APRS software running on the computer connected to the TNC is programmed with the station's position. The software sends the programmed position information to the TNC when required and the TNC relays the information to the radio for transmission. (Other APRS stations that receive the position packets display the location of the received station on their APRS maps.)

In a typical mobile APRS station, a Global Positioning System (GPS) receiver calculates the station position from signals received from GPS satellites, then sends the position to the TNC once per second. Alternatively, a computer can be used instead of a GPS receiver to provide position information for a mobile APRS station, but that requires an operator to enter each new position manually as the mobile station moves. For safety's sake, the operator of the mobile vehicle and the operator of the mobile APRS station should not be one and the same.

A mobile APRS station using a GPS receiver to provide position information may also use a computer running APRS software. In this case, the APRS software does not originate the position information. Instead, it relays the position information from the GPS to the TNC when required and it is also displays its position and the position of other received APRS stations on its APRS maps.

A home base APRS station does not require a GPS receiver because it does not change position. (When the APRS software of a home base APRS station is initially configured, a GPS receiver may be used to determine the station's location. On a day-to-day basis, however, a GPS receiver is not required at home.)

TNC Requirements

If you plan to use a computer in your APRS station, then any TNC that is compatible with the original TAPR TNC-2 design is also compatible with APRS. Virtually every new TNC sold since 1985 falls into this category, so you should not have any problem finding a suitable TNC for APRS operation with a computer.

If you plan to do APRS without a computer, that is, with a GPS receiver connected to a TNC, however, then the TNC must be GPS compatible. The March 1994 release of TAPR TNC-2 firmware added support for GPS operation, so if your TNC is compatible with that firmware release, then you may run APRS without a computer.

Beyond GPS compatibility, there are TNCs that offer more with regard to APRS support, especially if your APRS station will be a "wide" digipeater, that is, a digipeater providing coverage for a wide geographic area on a full time basis. Recent models of Kantronics and PacComm TNC firmware provide APRS support. In addition, the PacComm firmware may be installed in TAPR TNC-2 compatible TNCs like the MFJ-1270 series.

In brief, the firmware allows your station to use more than one alias as well as new protocols that provide more efficiency with regard to digipeater paths (the "APRS Digipeaters" section of the next chapter describes this firmware support in detail). If you are planning to put a wide digipeater on the air, you should seriously consider the firmware upgrade, especially if other wide digipeaters in your area are using the features provided by the firmware.

Computer Requirements

The requirements of the computer you intend to use for APRS vary depending upon the version of APRS you intend to use—the *DOS* version, a *Windows* version, the *Mac OS* version, or the Palm III version.

APRS (DOS)

The minimum requirements for *APRS (DOS)* are a PC running *DOS* with an 8088 microprocessor (or better), a standard CGA, EGA or VGA monitor, and 550 kbytes of free RAM. *APRS (DOS)* does not work with nonstandard video cards, such as the Hercules video card.

APRS+SA (Windows version)

APRS+SA is a *Windows* version of APRS that requires a PC running *Windows 95, 98* or *NT.*

WinAPRS (Windows version)

The minimum requirements for the *Windows* version of APRS, *WinAPRS*, are a PC with a 386 microprocessor running *Windows 95*. A PC with a 486 microprocessor, 33-MHz clock and 8 Mbytes of RAM running *Windows 95, Windows NT* or *Windows 3.1* is recommended.

MacAPRS (Mac OS version)

At a minimum, the *Mac OS* version of APRS, *MacAPRS*, requires a Macintosh computer running System 7.0 or later. A color monitor and 8 Mbytes of RAM are recommended.

pocketAPRS (Palm III version)

pocketAPRS requires a 3Com Palm III Connected Organizer, which is a hand-held personal digital assistant (PDA). Other models of the Palm PDA can also run *pocketAPRS* if they use *Palm OS* v3.0.

Radio Equipment Requirements

APRS does not require any special radio equipment. If your Amateur Radio station performs well with other packet radio applications, then it should perform well with APRS.

Of course, the radio equipment must be capable of transmitting and receiving signals on the bands you intend to operate. With this in mind, you need radio equipment that operates on two radio bands if you intend to operate a gateway APRS station. This scenario typically requires an HF transceiver and a VHF or UHF transceiver.

GPS Receiver Requirements

The APRS requirement for a GPS receiver is simple. The GPS receiver must output data in the format specified by National Marine Electronics Association (NMEA) standard NMEA-0183. In fact, any navigational equipment (such as LORAN) that outputs data in NMEA-0183 format will also work with APRS. Note that some aeronautical GPS equipment does not output NMEA-0183 formatted data.

Once you meet the NMEA-0183 data format requirement, it is your choice as to what kind of GPS receiver to purchase. For mobile and portable APRS applications, the size, weight and power requirements of the GPS receiver should be a consideration. The smaller, the better should be your goal. A GPS receiver that fits in a TNC would do it!

Some GPS receivers have built-in displays that indicate your position. These displays may be used as a substitute for a computer display of APRS maps. For example, the Garmin II PLUS and III GPS receivers not only display your position, but also display the position of other APRS stations that you receive (if your TNC is configured to send that information to the GPS receiver). In such a configuration, you are able to determine how your position relates to the location of other APRS stations in your area. In addition, the Garmin III allows you to load road maps from an optional CD-ROM. These maps are displayed along with the position information to provide a display that is competitive with APRS maps displayed by a computer.

Another consideration for mobile and portable applications

is the antenna options of the GPS receiver. With APRS GPS applications, you now have to worry about two antennas, one for your radio equipment and one for the GPS receiver. Again, the smaller, the better should be your goal. A GPS receiver with a self-contained antenna is your best choice.

INTERCONNECTION OF BASIC COMPONENTS

The following paragraphs describe how to interconnect the basic components of the APRS station—the TNC, radio, computer and GPS receiver.

Radio-to-TNC Connection

The radio side of the TNC is the simpler connection. The TNC radio port, which is typically a female DB-9 or 5-pin DIN connector, provides connections for audio output, audio input, press-to-talk (PTT) and ground.

Connect the audio output of the TNC to the audio input of your transmitter/transceiver. Typically, the audio input of your radio equipment is the microphone input (MIC) connection, but some transceivers have separate audio inputs for AFSK tones (sometimes labeled "AFSK in"). If such a connection is available, it is better to use that connection rather than the microphone input because you will not have to disconnect the TNC from the microphone connector whenever you want to use the radio in the voice mode. In addition, the AFSK input may bypass circuits in the transceiver that are intended for voice and/ or may insert circuits intended for data. Voice circuits are not necessarily beneficial to data transmission, so bypassing them is a good thing. On the other hand, circuits intended to improve data transmission should be used whenever possible.

Connect the audio input of the TNC to the audio output of your receiver/transceiver. Typically, the audio output of your radio is a speaker or headphone connector, but some radios have optional audio outputs (sometimes labeled "AFSK out"). Again, connection to such an optional audio output avoids TNC disconnection when you switch to voice and may bypass circuits intended for processing voice and/ or insert circuits intended for processing data. If your radio does not have separate AFSK jacks, the phone patch input and output jacks often provide an acceptable alternative.

Connect the PTT line of the TNC to a PTT connection on your transmitter/transceiver. Usually, PTT is available at the microphone connector, but the PTT line is sometimes brought out to another connector as well. Again, connection to the optional PTT jack is preferable; this avoids cable changes when you switch modes.

Finally, connect the TNC ground to the ground connection accompanies the other connections to your transceiver (or transmitter and receiver), that is, the ground that accompanies the radio's MIC, PTT, speaker or AFSK In/Out connections. (**Figure 2-1** illustrates the typical TNC-to-radio connection.)

The only complication in making connections on the radio side of the TNC is when the radio is a VHF or UHF handheld transceiver that uses a common conductor for audio input (MIC) and PTT. Simply connecting the TNC audio output and PTT leads to the common connection on the radio will not work.

To make the connection successfully, a resistor and a capacitor, are required as illustrated in **Figure 2-2**. Resistor and capacitor values of 1 kΩ to 2 kΩ and 0.01 to 1.0 µF are typical, but these values depend on the radio used, so consult the manual that accompanies your radio for the values that are required.

Computer/GPS-to-TNC Connection

The serial port of the TNC connects to the computer and/or GPS receiver.

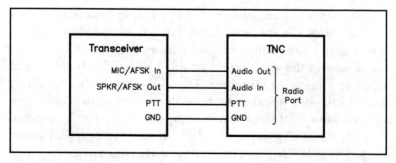

Figure 2-1—The typical radio-to-TNC connection requires four connections.

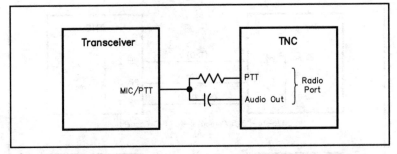

Figure 2-2—When the radio uses a common MIC/PTT conductor, the radio-to-TNC connection requires a resistor and capacitor to isolate the signals at the TNC.

Computer-to-TNC

The serial ports of most TNCs are compatible with Electronic Industries Association (EIA) interface standard EIA-232. This standard defines 25 signals that may be transferred via the interface. However, the TNC needs only three of those signals to communicate with a computer and GPS receiver: Transmitted Data, Received Data and Signal Ground.

In most cases, the TNC uses a female 25-pin D-type (DB-25) connector for the serial port. This necessitates using a male DB-25 connector with pins 2, 3 and 7 cabled to a connector that mates with the serial port of the computer or GPS receiver.

The computer typically has a male DB-25 or male 9-pin D-type (DB-9) connector for its serial port. This necessitates using a female DB-25 or DB-9 connector at the computer end of the computer-to-TNC connection. For DB-25-to-DB-25 cabling, pins 2, 3 and 7 (Transmitted Data, Received Data and Signal Ground) are connected between each DB-25 connector, as illustrated in **Figure 2-3a**.

For DB-25-to-DB-9 cabling, pins 2 and 3 (Transmitted Data and Received Data) are connected between each connector and pin 7 (Signal Ground) of the DB-25 is connected to pin 5 of the DB-9, as illustrated in Figure 2-3b. To avoid the time and expense of building a cable for the computer-to-TNC connection, you can use the cable connecting your computer serial port to your external telephone line modem, if you have one.

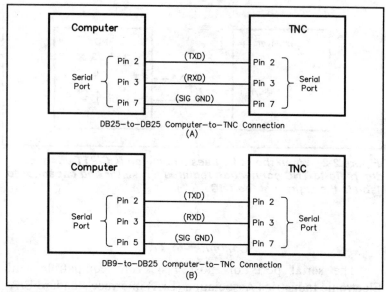

Figure 2-3—The minimal cabling for TNC-to-computer connections requires three wires.

Since the TNC's serial port is EIA-232 compatible, it is compatible with the serial ports of most computers and GPS receivers—with the notable exception of Macintosh computers. Until recently, Macs used an EIA-422 interface for their serial ports. This does not pose a big problem and only requires a male DB-25-to-Macintosh serial port cable to complete the connection. Recent Macs use a Universal Serial Bus (USB) instead of the EIA-422 interface, however. Although adapters are available to permit you to connect a serial port device (such as a TNC) to the Mac's USB, MacAPRS does not support USB as this is written.

GPS-to-TNC

For the TNC-to-GPS connection, you use the same connector and cabling at the TNC end that you use for the TNC-to-computer connection (typically, a male DB-25 with wire connections at pins 2, 3 and 7). However, there is no typical connector for the GPS end of this connection. Different GPS receivers use different types of connectors. For example, Garmin GPS receivers use a unique 4-pin connector (refer to the sidebar, "Garmin GPS Connectors"). Other brands of GPS receivers use other types of connectors. Therefore, you must obtain the appropriate connector for the GPS receiver you intend to use and wire it correctly to the TNC connector. The documentation accompanying your GPS receiver should provide the pin-out for the connector.

Computer AND GPS-to-TNC

The computer-to-TNC connection is fine if you do not intend to use a GPS receiver in your APRS application, for

Garmin GPS Connectors

Garmin GPS receivers are popular and, as a result, they are a popular choice for APRS applications. A drawback with Garmin is the unique 4-pin connector that is used for its data port. Garmin does not sell the connector. Instead, they sell expensive PC interface cables with the connector molded onto the cable. To get a connector, you had to purchase the cable.

Garmin enthusiasts sought an alternative and one such fellow, named Larry, built a mold to make his own Garmin-compatible connectors. Since he only needed a few for himself, he decided to make the connector available to other enthusiasts. At last count, he has distributed 42,794 connectors. If you have a Garmin and would like one or two of Larry's connectors, surf the Internet to **http://pfranc.com/projects/g45contr/g45_idx.htm** and connect it to your TNC as illustrated in **Figure 2-A**.

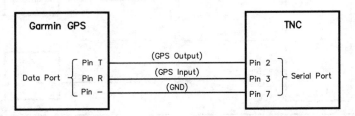

Figure 2-A—The Garmin GPS-to-TNC (DB-25) connection requires three wires and Larry's connector.

example, in a home base installation. And the GPS-to-computer connection is suitable if you do not intend to use a computer in your APRS application, for example, in a tracker installation. If you intend to use both a computer and a GPS receiver, however, you must make different connections.

If your computer has two serial ports available, then use the cabling described in "Computer-to-TNC" above to connect your TNC to one port. Use the cabling described in "GPS-to-TNC" above to connect your GPS receiver to the other port, then configure your APRS software so that it is aware of these connections, which are illustrated in **Figure 2-4**.

If your computer has only one serial port available, then you can use a hardware single port switch (HSP) cable, which is available from a number of sources (Kantronics, MFJ,

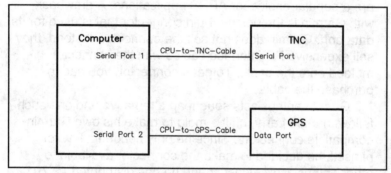

Figure 2-4—Connecting a TNC and a GPS receiver to a computer is straightforward when the computer has two serial ports.

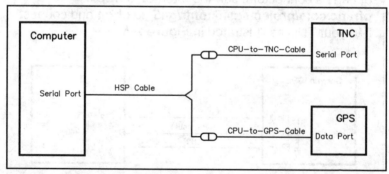

Figure 2-5—Connecting a TNC and a GPS receiver to a computer requires a hardware single port switch (HSP) cable when the computer has only one serial port.

PacComm). Simply, connect the HSP cable to the serial port of your computer, then use the cabling described earlier to connect your TNC and GPS receiver to the HSP cable, as illustrated in **Figure 2-5**.

If your computer has only one serial port, an alternative to the HSP cable is available if your TNC is a Kantronics KPC-3 Plus with firmware version 8.3 or later or a PacComm PicoPacket TNC with dual serial ports. In either case, you connect the GPS to the TNC instead of your computer.

If your TNC is a Kantronics KPC-3 Plus with firmware version 8.3 or later, you connect your computer to the TNC as described in "Computer-to-TNC" above. Connect the computer to the male DB-25 connector at the TNC end via its pins 2, 3 and 7 (Transmitted Data, Received Data and Signal Ground). Instead of connecting the GPS receiver to the KPC-3 Plus serial port, you connect it to the TNC's radio port with the GPS output connected to pin 2 and GPS ground to pin 6, as illustrated in **Figure 2-6**. The radio connections to the radio port remain the same.

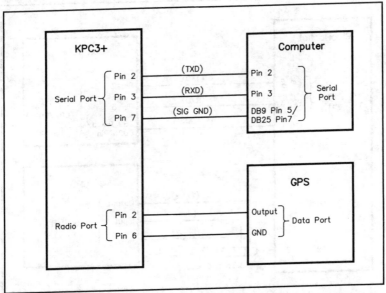

Figure 2-6—If your TNC is a Kantronics KPC-3 Plus with firmware version 8.3, you can connect your computer to its serial port and the GPS receiver to its radio port.

When you program the TNC, you must enable this GPS connection via the GPSPORT command (for example, GPSPORT 4800 NORMAL CHECKSUM). You must also disable external carrier detect via the CD command (CD INTERNAL or CD SOFTWARE).

If your TNC is a PacComm PicoPacket with the dual serial port option, you connect your computer to one serial port via an RJ-45 plug and your GPS receiver to the other serial port via a 3.5 mm stereo plug. (The PicoPacket uses RJ-45 connectors for its first serial port and its radio port.) These connections are illustrated in **Figure 2-7**. Another alternative is to use a PacComm PicoPacket TNC with the internal GPS receiver option. In this case, you only have to connect the TNC to your radio and computer.

Kenwood TH-D7A Connections

There are two ways you can use the Kenwood TH-D7 transceiver for APRS: as a standalone APRS station by means of

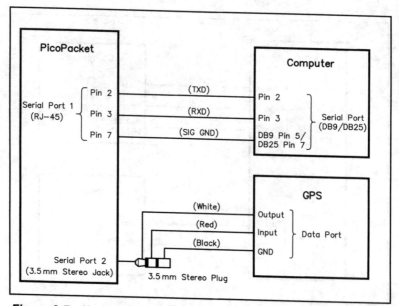

Figure 2-7—If your TNC is a PacComm PicoPacket with dual serial ports, you can connect your computer to one serial port and the GPS receiver to the other serial port.

its built-in APRS software or as the radio and TNC portion of an APRS station by configuring its built-in TNC using any version of APRS.

As a standalone APRS station, you have to make a connection to the radio only if you are using a GPS receiver. In that case, you use the cable with the 2.5 mm 3-conductor plug that was included with the TH-D7. Connect the red wire in the cable to the GPS data output, connect the white wire to the GPS data input and connect the shield to GPS ground. Then, connect the 3-conductor plug to the GPS port of the TH-D7. **Figure 2-8** illustrates this connection.

To use the TH-D7 with a version of APRS running on a computer, connect the radio to the computer with the optional Kenwood PG-4W cable. Connect the 3-conductor plug of the PG-4W to the PC port of the radio and connect the DB-9 connector to the serial port of your computer. If the serial port your computer is not a DB-9, you must acquire an adapter (for example, a DB-9-to-DB-25 adapter for DB-25 serial ports) to complete the connection.

If you plan to use a GPS receiver in this configuration, connect the GPS receiver to the TH-D7 as described above and illustrated in Figure 2-8.

Palm III PDA Connections

The 3Com Palm III PDA may be connected to a TNC that has a DB-25 serial port connector by means of the optional Palm modem cable. Unfortunately, 3Com discontinued this cable, but

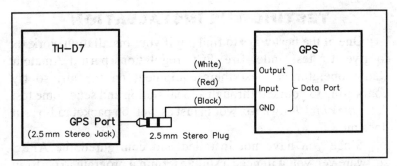

Figure 2-8—Use the cable included with the Kenwood TH-D7 to connect a GPS receiver.

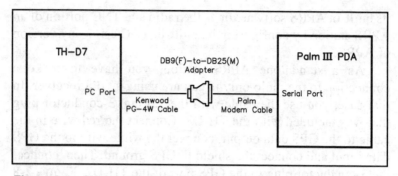

Figure 2-9—Mating the Palm III PDA to the Kenwood TH-D7 transceiver requires two cables and a DB-9(female)-to-DB-25(male) adapter.

an alternative cable manufactured by Swann Communications (of Australia) is available from New World Technologies (110 Greene St, Suite 5100, New York, NY 10012, **http://www.nwt.com**). In either case, you simply connect the modem cable to the DB-25 serial port of the TNC and the serial port of the Palm III.

Rather than connecting the Palm III to a TNC, a popular configuration using the PDA is connecting it to the Kenwood TH-D7 transceiver. In this case, you connect the modem cable to the serial port of the Palm III. Connect the optional Kenwood PG-4W cable to the PC port of the TH-D7. Then, mate the two cables together with a DB-25 (male)-to-DB-9 (female) adapter. **Figure 2-9** illustrates this connection.

TESTING THE INSTALLATION

One of the best ways to find out if your installation works is to give it a test under fire. FCC regulations permit Amateur Radio operators to test their equipment on the air, so try connecting to yourself through a local station and send some test data (*the quick brown fox* works just as well on packet radio as it does on RTTY).

Since you have not installed and configured the APRS software yet, you will need a simple terminal program to perform the test. *Hyperterminal*, which is an Accessories program included in *Windows 95/98/NT*, is adequate for this purpose. For other computer platforms, you can use a public domain terminal program that is suitable.

After you have the terminal software up and running, try connecting to yourself. To do so, the other station you are connecting through must have its digipeater function enabled (DIGI ON). If it is disabled, you can still obtain some test results because if your installation is working, you will at least be able to connect and disconnect from that station.

To connect to yourself, at the TNC command prompt, type:

C *URCALL* V *THRCALL* <Enter>

where ***URCALL*** is your call sign and SSID (if any) and ***THRCALL*** is the call sign and SSID (if any) of the station through which you are trying to digipeat.

If you are able to connect with yourself and successfully receive the test data, your installation is working. Go to the next section of this book and have fun!

If you are unable to connect with yourself (or worse), read further for the possible solution to the problem.

Troubleshooting Your Installation

You don't have to be a rocket scientist to figure out why your installation is not working. All you need is a little help from your friendly troubleshooting guide, which is presented below.

Assuming that your TNC is functioning properly, that is, it was not dead on arrival or is not on the verge of death, then this troubleshooting guide will be able to diagnose the majority of problems you are likely to encounter with your installation.

If your packet radio controller is a multiport and/or multimode controller, that adds complexity to trouble-shooting your installation, complexity that is not covered by the guide. If the troubleshooting guide is unable to solve the problem in a multiport and/or multimode environment, then check that the problem is not related to selecting the incorrect port or incorrect mode. Your equipment manual may offer some assistance.

Table 2-1
Troubleshooting Guide

Trouble

Nothing happens after turning on the TNC power switch.

No sign-on message after power-up; front panel indicators are lit.

Sign-on message is garbled.

TNC does not respond to keyboard input.

Cannot copy packets from other stations; DCD front panel indicator does not light when signal is heard.

Cannot copy packets from other stations; DCD front panel indicator lights when signal is heard.

Cannot copy packets from other stations; DCD front panel indicator lights when signal is heard; garbled characters appear on computer display.

Transmitter does not key although PTT indicator lights.

Transmitter is keyed continuously.

Other stations cannot copy your packets, but you can copy their packets.

Possible Causes

Power source problem; check connection between TNC and power supply; check that connection is tight; check connection wiring; check that an external switch (such as a wall switch) that controls the power supply is not turned off.

Connection between TNC and computer serial port; check that connection is tight; check the Received Data (pin 3) and Signal Ground (DB-25 pin 7/DB-9 pin 5) leads.

Incompatibility between TNC and computer serial port; check that the serial port data rate, parity and character bit length of the TNC and computer serial port are equal.

Connection between TNC and computer serial port; check that connection is tight; check the Transmitted Data (pin 2) and Signal Ground (DB-25 pin 7/DB-9 pin 5) leads.

Connection between TNC and radio; check that connection is tight; check the connection between the TNC audio input and radio audio output.

Receiver audio is set too low; turn up the volume.

Connection between TNC and computer serial port; check that connection is tight; check the Received Data lead, pin 3.

Receiver audio is set too high; turn down the volume.

Incompatibility between TNC and channel activity; check that the radio port data rate, parity and character bit length of the TNC and other stations on the air are equal.

Connection between TNC and radio; check that connection is tight; check the PTT and ground leads.

Connection between TNC and radio; check that connection is tight; check the PTT and ground leads.

Connection between TNC and radio; check that connection is tight; check the connection between the TNC audio output and radio audio input.

TNC audio output is set incorrectly; check deviation (refer to "Deviation" section below).

TXdelay is set too low; increase TXdelay by 10 ms increments.

Internal Diagnostics

Some TNCs provide their own self-contained diagnostics. Check the TNC manual to find out what, if anything, is available and, if all else fails, try them.

Deviation

In the FM mode, frequency information is encoded by varying the carrier frequency of the FM signal, while amplitude is encoded by controlling the amount that the carrier frequency is varied or deviated. This change, shift or deviation of the carrier frequency is proportional to the amplitude of the input signal. If the amplitude of the input signal is zero, there will be no change (no deviation) in the carrier frequency and there will be nothing heard in the receiver at the other end. As the amplitude of the input signal increases, the amount by which the carrier shifts (or deviates) increases, too.

For this explanation, let us assume that each volt of amplitude corresponds to 1 kHz of deviation. Therefore, if you modulate a 1500 Hz tone at a carrier frequency of 147.000 MHz with 2 volts of amplitude, the carrier will deviate 2 kHz, that is, between 146.999 and 147.001 MHz. If you modulate the same tone at the same carrier frequency with 4 volts of amplitude, the carrier will deviate 4 kHz (between 146.998 and 147.002 MHz).

Ideally, the deviation of your signal should fall between 3.0 and 3.5 kHz. It will be hard to decode your packets if your signal is below 3.0 kHz of deviation. The TNC at the other end cannot decode your packets if it can't hear them! On the other hand, it will be difficult to decode your packets if your deviation is too much above 3.5 kHz. Your transmitter can not deviate signals much higher than that. Too high a deviation causes your signal to be clipped by the audio stages of your transmitter and results in a distorted signal in the receiver at the other end of the connection, that is, a signal that a TNC will have a tough time decoding.

To achieve the best throughput of your packets, you must set your FM signal deviation within the ideal range. To do this, you need a deviation meter and an alignment tool that allows you to adjust the audio output level control of your TNC. (Some TNCs like the Kantronics KPC-3 Plus, allow you to adjust the level in software.)

To check the deviation of your transmitter, connect it to a dummy load and start transmitting a dead carrier, that is, without audio input, while you attempt to tune in your signal with the deviation meter. If the meter has a speaker output, I recommend attaching a speaker to it to simplify the tuning procedure. With a speaker attached, you simply tune the meter until you hear the squelch break, then you continue tuning very slowly until you tune to the center of the signal.

Next, you put your TNC in the calibration mode by typing at the command prompt:

CAL ON <ENTER>

In the calibration mode, check the deviation as you transmit, in succession, the high and low frequency tones of the TNC (pressing your keyboard Space Bar switches between the high and low tones). If the deviation of a tone is too high or too low, adjust the level accordingly using the TNC audio output control. The location and accessibility of the audio output control varies with each TNC. Check your TNC manual for its location.

If your TNC does not have such a control, you will have to adjust the microphone gain of your transmitter. If that is the case, check the radio manual for the location and accessibility of that control. After you adjust the audio output control, check both tones again to make sure they are still adjusted correctly.

3

SOFTWARE INSTALLATION AND CONFIGURATION

This chapter describes how to install and configure the APRS software. APRS with and without a GPS receiver are the most common APRS configurations and those are the configurations described here.

The software installation and configuration procedures are divided into two parts. The first part describes the preliminary steps that apply to the installation and configuration of all versions of APRS. The second part describes the specific installation and configuration procedures as they apply to each version of APRS.

PRELIMINARY STEPS

The following describes the preliminary steps that apply to the installation and configuration of all versions of APRS. The second part describes the specific installation and configuration procedures as they apply to each version of APRS.

Getting Software

The first thing you need in order to install and configure APRS is APRS!

The primary source for APRS software is the Internet. You may obtain most versions of APRS from TAPR's Web site (its URL is **ftp://ftp.tapr.org/software_lib/aprssig**). You may also obtain *the* Macintosh, *Windows* and a second Linux version (*MacAPRS*, *WinAPRS* and *XAPRS*, respectively) from the Rutgers University Web site. Its URL is **ftp://aprs.rutgers.edu/**

pub/hamradio/APRS. In addition to the APRS software, these sites also store the map files that may be used with APRS.

To get the software on disk, contact the APRS authors.

For *APRS (DOS)*, contact Bob Bruninga, WB4APR, at 115 Old Farm Ct, Glen Burnie, MD 21060, email **bruninga@ nadn.navy.mil**.

For *APRS+SA*, contact Brent Hildebrand, KH2Z, at 1748 Chaparral Rd, Redlands, CA 92373, email **bhildebrand@ earthlink.net**.

For *MacAPRS*, contact Keith Sproul, WU2Z, at 698 Magnolia Rd, North Brunswick, NJ 08902, email **ksproul@ rci.rutgers.edu**.

For *pocketAPRS*, contact Mike Musick, NØQBF, at PO Box 8469, Olivette, MO 63132, email **mcmusick@anet-stl.com**.

For *WinAPRS*, contact Mark Sproul, KB2ICI, at 698 Magnolia Rd, North Brunswick, NJ 08902, email **sproul@ap.org**.

Future Software

At the time of this writing, there are three new versions of APRS that are under development, two *Linux* operating system versions and a version for handheld computers running the *Windows CE* operating system.

One *Linux* version is *XASTIR*, which is being developed by Frank Giannandrea, KCØDGE, (436 Juniper Ln, Bailey, CO 80421, email **fgiannan@eazy.net**). You may obtain a beta test copy of *XASTIR* from **http://www.eazy.net/users/fgiannan/linux/docs/**.

Another *Linux* version is *XAPRS*, which is being produced by Keith and Mark Sproul (contact Mark, KB2ICI, at 698 Magnolia Rd, North Brunswick, NJ 08902, email **sproul @ap.org**). Beta test copies of *XAPRS* are available from **ftp://ftp.tapr.org/software_lib/aprssig** and **ftp://aprs. rutgers.edu/pub/hamradio/APRS**.

The Sproul Brothers are using the *MacAPRS/WinAPRS* source code to develop *XAPRS*, so the final product should have a feature set similar to its Macintosh and Windows lineage.

The *Windows CE* version is *APRS/CE* and it is being developed by Rob Wittner, KZ5RW (931B South Main St 201, Kernersville, NC 27284, e-mail **aprsce@iwhereto.com**).

A beta test version of *APRS/CE* was not available at the time of this writing, but its features list includes the ability to run on all Handheld PCs (H/PCs), Palm-size PCs (P/PCs) and Handheld PC Pros (H/PC Pros) running *Windows CE* version 2.0 or later. It supports grayscale and color maps on the handheld devices and it can use all *MacAPRS*, *pocketAPRS* and *WinAPRS* maps (memory permitting). It also supports multiple serial connections for simultaneous reception of TNC and GPS data. Its map display provides a continuous range of magnification from the entire earth to one pixel (equal to 1.5 inches). Color icons, weather display and track history are shown. *APRS/CE* also has full message and bulletin capabilities, support for adding and display objects, and for those units with Internet connectivity, the ability to connect to the APRServers.

Station Coordinates

As they say in the real estate business, "location, location, location." The same can be said for APRS. You need to know your exact location and configure APRS with that information in order for APRS to operate as accurately as possible.

A city, town or street address is not accurate enough. Rather, you need your station coordinates, that is, the latitude and longitude of your APRS station, preferably in degrees, minutes and seconds. There are a few ways to obtain this information.

An easy, accurate, but expensive way to obtain your station coordinates is by using a GPS receiver that provides that information. If you know someone who has a GPS receiver and is willing to help you out, then you have a substantial economic savings without forgoing the ease and accuracy of determining your coordinates. If you purchased a GPS receiver to use with APRS, then you have it made. However, I would not advise purchasing a GPS receiver just to obtain your station coordinates for the sake of APRS accuracy. There are less expensive and still accurate ways of determining your coordinates.

You can look it up. Using a good map of your area, you can determine your coordinates with fairly good accuracy. Topographic maps like the 7.5-minute quadrangles published by the United States Geological Survey (USGS, Washington, DC 20242) are perfect for determining your coordinates. The USGS maps are inexpensive and very detailed. If you don't live in an urban area, the building that houses your APRS station likely appears on the USGS quadrangle for your area. So, that should permit you to determine your coordinates accurately.

You can also look up your coordinates in an atlas. The maps in an atlas are not as detailed as the USGS quadrangles, so determining your coordinates using a map in an atlas produces less accurate results. You can use those results as a starting point and fine tune them later, however.

Some atlases list the major cities and towns in the world and sometimes the latitude and longitude of each city and town is also listed. Some almanacs provide similar lists, but only for the major cities. The accuracy of such lists varies depending on how close you live to the location in your town or city where the coordinates were determined. If you live over the town hall or post office, you are in pretty good shape using the coordinates from an atlas or almanac. If you live on the back forty of Old Macdonald's farm, however, the coordinates may be bit off.

If you are on the Internet, you can obtain your coordinates from the Geographic Name Server run by the Geography Department of Rutgers University. Simply **telnet://geogns.rutgers.edu:3000/** and after the server start-up message appears, enter your location. In a few seconds, the server provides you with information concerning your location including its latitude and longitude in degrees, minutes and seconds. For example, when I entered Wolcott, CT, the server responded with the following:

Wolcott (name of place)
CT (state)
New Haven (county)
413608N (latitude)
0725914W (longitude)
Southington (topological map)
Unknown (elevation)
Unknown (population)

Height Above Average Terrain (HAAT)

While configuring APRS, you will be prompted to enter your station's Height Above Average Terrain (HAAT). APRS uses HAAT to calculate and display your station's coverage on the APRS maps.

HAAT is not the same as your height above sea level. HAAT is the height of your antenna as it relates to the average height of the terrain in the 10-mile radius surrounding your station's antenna. For example, if your antenna is 1000 feet above sea level and the average height of the terrain in the 10-mile radius surrounding the antenna is 900 feet, your HAAT is 100 feet.

To calculate HAAT, use a topographical map and record the height of the terrain in 2-mile increments along the eight compass directions (N, NE, E, SE, S, SW, W and NW) radiating 10 miles out from your antenna. For example, in the northeast direction, you would record the height of the terrain at the points that are 2, 4, 6, 8 and 10 miles northeast of your antenna.

When you are finished, you should have 40 points recorded. Add them together and divide the sum by 40. The result of this calculation is the average height of the terrain in the 10-mile radius surrounding your station. Subtract this figure from the height of your antenna above sea level. The difference is your HAAT.

Selecting Digipeater (Unproto) Paths

The AX.25 Unproto command determines the digipeaters used to propagate the packets transmitted by your APRS station. For example, if Unproto is set to VIA A,B, your packet is initially retransmitted by digipeater A. Then, it is retransmitted by digipeater B (assuming that digipeater B hears digipeater A's retransmission of your packet). In this example, your "digipeater path" is VIA A,B or simply, A,B.

The digipeater path that your APRS station uses is critical to its ability to be received by other APRS stations. If your path is set incorrectly, then only the stations that can hear you directly will hear you, while the stations beyond the range of your transmissions won't hear you. For example, if your path is A,B, but digipeater A can't hear you, then none of the digipeaters in your path will retransmit your packets.

APRS simplifies the selection of your digipeater path by means of the alias command that is included in the firmware of your TNC. (Alias permits a packet station to use one or more station identifications in addition to the identification, typically, the station call sign, that is programmed into the TNC via the MYCall command.)

In theory, all APRS stations may be used to relay the packets of less fortunate APRS stations, i.e., stations running less power, less antenna, and in less favorable locations. So, it is suggested that all APRS stations use an alias of RELAY.

If your digipeater path is RELAY,A,B instead of A,B your chances of getting your packets retransmitted by digipeaters A and B is enhanced. Any APRS RELAY station that hears your initial packet will retransmit it. Assuming that one of those RELAY stations is more fortunate than your station, i.e., more power, more antenna and more HAAT, then digipeater A is more likely to hear a RELAY's retransmission of your packet (and digipeater A will retransmit it, too).

To further simplify matters, it is suggested that APRS digipeaters use an alias of WIDE (for wide area digipeater). In the RELAY,A,B digipeater path example, if your packet was retransmitted by one or more RELAYs, your packet would go no further if digipeater A could not hear any of the RELAYs. But, what if another digipeater (C, D or E) heard one of the RELAYs? If C, D or E was a WIDE digipeater and your path was RELAY,WIDE, instead of RELAY,A,B then your packet would be retransmitted by WIDE C, D and/or E.

When you configure your APRS software, you can ignore the digipeater path setting and let the software use its default path. The default settings of your packet paths allow you to get up and running without having an intimate knowledge of your local APRS network. Depending on the version of APRS you are using, the default path is typically either RELAY or WIDE, or a combination of RELAY and WIDE.

On the other hand, you may fine-tune the digipeater path setting to be compatible with local APRS network, especially after you become familiar with your local APRS network. For example, if you know which RELAYs and WIDEs can hear your station, program the actual call signs of the RELAY and WIDE stations into your path rather than using aliases. This promotes network efficiency and throughput. If your path is A,B instead of RELAY,WIDE, instead of hitting two or more RELAYs or WIDEs and causing packet collisions, you will hit only A, then only B, thus, reducing the potential for collision and increasing throughput. This applies to all fixed stations and any mobile stations that travel the same, short distance on a regular basis. Mobile stations passing through an unfamiliar APRS network are a different matter. They should stick with generic paths like RELAY,WIDE.

APRS Digipeaters

Any fixed APRS station can serve as an APRS digipeater and is encouraged to do so in order to fill in the nooks and crannies of the APRS network. Well-situated, that is, highly elevated, fixed APRS stations are encouraged to serve as wide digipeaters in order to fill in the wide expanses of the APRS network.

The alias of a fixed APRS station that is not a wide digipeater should be set to RELAY and its path should be set to WIDE,WIDE. The alias of a wide digipeater should be set to WIDE and its path should be set to WIDE,WIDE.

Ideally, wide digipeaters should use a current generation TNC that may be configured with multiple aliases. One alias should be set to RELAY and another alias to WIDE. In this way, a wide digipeater can also fill in as a RELAY digipeater for those nooks and crannies not covered by other RELAY digipeaters.

A work-around for TNCs with only one alias is to set the call sign to RELAY (with the MYCall command), set the alias to WIDE (with the MYAlias command), and let the Beacon function of the TNC take care of the legal identification requirements. The only negative aspect about using this work-around is that your station icon appears on the APRS maps with a label of RELAY or WIDE rather than your call sign. If you do use this work-around, make sure to include your call sign in the beacon (with the BText command) and to configure the beacon to be sent every 10 minutes or less (with Beacon Every command).

Beyond multiple aliases, later advancements in digipeater functionality have promoted further APRS network efficiency.

The digipeating call sign substitution function was added in 1997. When this function is enabled, the digipeater replaces the alias in a received packet with its own call sign before it digipeats it. This permits other stations to trace the path of a digipeated packet.

For example, if digipeater WA1LOU-15 has WIDE as an alias and it receives a packet with a path of RELAY,WIDE, it replaces the WIDE with WA1LOU-15 if call sign substitution is enabled. When it digipeats that packet, the path of that packet is RELAY,WA1LOU-15. Anyone receiving the packet can trace it to WA1LOU-15, instead of trying to determine which WIDE repeated it.

Besides the ability to trace packet paths, this function also improves network efficiency by preventing digipeaters from repeating a packet it has already transmitted. Digipeaters with call sign substitution enabled often identify themselves as having that capability by setting one of their aliases to TRACE.

The WIDEn-n function was added in 1998. When this function is enabled on a network-wide basis, stations can use a path of WIDE3-3, for example, instead of WIDE,WIDE,WIDE, thus promoting network efficiency by having shorter packets (the path is only seven bytes long no matter how many digipeaters are in it).

When a WIDEn-n digipeater receives a packet with a WIDEn-n path, it decrements the -n before it digipeats it. Thus, a WIDE3-3 packet becomes a WIDE3-2 packet when it is initially digipeated. Subsequent digipeats result in WIDE3-1 and WIDE3-0 packets. When -n becomes -0, the packet will not be digipeated.

The TRACEn-n function was also added in 1998. It is similar to the WIDEn-n function in that when it is enabled, it decrements the -n before repeating a packet.

TRACEn-n differs from WIDEn-n in that it also inserts its call sign in the path of the packet to permit other stations to trace the path of a digipeated packet. Although TRACEn-n promotes the ability to trace packet paths, it reduces network efficiency because the length of the packet increases each time it is digipeated (by the number of bytes in the digipeater call sign plus one for the comma). For this reason, TRACEn-n should be used when the ability to trace packet paths is necessary.

Fixed APRS Stations

Each non-digipeater fixed APRS station should fine-tune its path for compatibility with its local APRS network once it becomes familiar with that network.

Rather than using the generic path of RELAY or WIDE, the path should be set with the call sign of the nearest digipeater that the fixed station uses to get its packets out into the network. In order to minimize duplication of effort, this is especially critical in areas where the fixed APRS station accesses two or more digipeaters with its RELAY or WIDE path.

The preferable path for a fixed station is to use the call sign of the nearest accessible digipeater followed by one or two WIDEs (CALLSIGN,WIDE or CALLSIGN,WIDE,WIDE, or in WIDEn-n APRS networks, CALLSIGN,WIDE1-1 or CALLSIGN,WIDE2-2). In this way, the fixed APRS station gets its packets out of its neighborhood in the most efficient way, that is, directly to one digipeater serving its area (by means of the CALLSIGN portion of its path). Then that digipeater uses the WIDE portion of the path to propagate the packets of the fixed station out into the APRS network via digipeaters with aliases of WIDE.

Mobile APRS Stations

Ideally, if a mobile APRS station knows the lay of the APRS network that it traverses, it should use the same path rules that apply to fixed APRS stations; that is, the call sign of the nearest accessible digipeater followed by one or two WIDEs (CALLSIGN,WIDE or CALLSIGN,WIDE,WIDE, or in WIDEn-n APRS networks, CALLSIGN,WIDE1-1 or CALLSIGN,WIDE2-2).

Unless the mobile station traverses the same path regularly, it is difficult if not impossible for it to be intimately familiar with the APRS network it passes through. As a result, a different path rule applies to the typical mobile APRS station and that rule is simple: a mobile APRS station should set its path for RELAY or WIDE or RELAY,WIDE.

Paths to Avoid

When configuring your digipeater path, RELAY should only be used in the first slot of your path (RELAY,WIDE, not RELAY,RELAY or WIDE,RELAY). RELAYs are intended to fill the gap to a WIDE; that is, every RELAY should be able to access a WIDE, so in most cases, a path of RELAY,RELAY is not necessary. A path of WIDE,RELAY makes no sense in any scenario because if you are able to access a WIDE, you have no need for a RELAY, and furthermore, your packets will be heard by all the RELAYs that can hear the WIDE anyway. Using WIDE,RELAY will key up every APRS TNC in the state, causing TVI at home stations and blanking out 2-meter voice operations in all mobile stations.

Also avoid using more than two WIDEs in your digipeater path (WIDE,WIDE, not WIDE,WIDE,WIDE). More than two WIDEs cause packet Ping-Pong with the first WIDE repeating its own packet after it hears it being transmitted by the second WIDE.

On the other hand, a digipeater path of WIDE3-3 is permissible in a WIDEn-n or TRACEn-n APRS network where call sign substitution is enabled because such a network is designed to prevent packet Ping-Pong.

Software Registration

All versions of APRS are shareware. The philosophy of shareware is that you can try out the software for free to see if it is suitable for you. If you intend to continue using it, then you are obligated to register the software and pay a registration fee.

Unregistered APRS software is not fully functional. It lacks the ability to save its configuration. As a result, you must configure the software every time you start it.

When you register APRS software, you receive a registration number that you enter into the software and then it becomes fully functional. (Information on how to register the software is included with each flavor of APRS.)

INSTALLATION AND CONFIGURATION

The following procedures provide the specific installation and configuration instructions for each version of APRS, that is, *APRS (DOS)*, *APRS+SA*, *MacAPRS*, *pocketAPRS*, *WinAPRS*, *XAPRS* and *XASTIR*. These procedures are intended to get your APRS software up and running as fast as possible in the two most common APRS configurations: APRS with and without a GPS receiver.

APRS (DOS) Installation and Configuration

APRS is the *DOS* version of APRS written by Bob Bruninga, WB4APR.

The minimum computer requirements of *APRS* are a PC running *DOS* with an 8088 microprocessor (or better), a standard CGA, EGA or VGA monitor, and 550 kbytes of free RAM. *APRS* does not work with non-standard video cards, such as the Hercules video card.

APRS is distributed as a compressed file, *aprs###.zip*, where ### is the version number of the software, for example, *aprs840.zip*. Besides the *APRS* application, this compressed file also contains documentation and a sufficient sampling of maps to get you up and running.

To decompress *APRS*, use the shareware application *PKUNZIP*, which is available from **http://www.pkware.com**.

The following steps describe how to install and configure *APRS*. These steps assume that you are familiar with the operation of *DOS*.

1. Power up your computer.
2. Create a new directory for *APRS* on your computer hard disk (type **MD APRS**, then press **Enter**).

   Change directories to the new directory you created in the previous step (type **CD APRS**, then press **Enter**).

   If the compressed (zipped) *APRS* is on a diskette, insert the diskette containing *APRS* into the A: drive, then decompress *APRS* using *PKUNZIP*. (Assuming *PKUNZIP* is on the C: drive, type **c:\pkunzip -d a:*aprs###***, then press **Enter**).

   If the compressed (zipped) *APRS* is already on your computer hard disk, decompress *APRS* using *PKUNZIP*. (Assuming the compressed *APRS* file and *PKUNZIP* are on the C: drive, type **c:\pkunzip -d c:*aprs###***, then press **Enter**).

   That completes the installation of *APRS*. Now you can configure *APRS* according to the following steps. Remember that if you have not registered *APRS*, you must configure the software each time you start it.

1. Assuming that your computer is already on, power up the rest of your APRS hardware (TNC, radio equipment and GPS receiver, if any).
2. Tune the radio to the local APRS operating frequency (144.39, 445.925 and 10.1515 MHz are the national APRS operating frequencies) and APRS mode (FM on VHF and UHF, LSB on HF).

3. Start APRS (type **aprs###**, then press **Enter**).
4. After the APRS start-up screen appears, as illustrated in **Figure 3-1**, the program prompts you for the following information:

   a. At the call sign prompt, type your call sign, then press **Enter**. Remember to enter an SSID if one is desired. An SSID (for secondary station identifier) is a number (0-15) that follows a packet radio station call sign (and a hyphen). It is used to differentiate between two or more packet radio stations operating under the same call sign. For example, my APRS digipeater is WA1LOU-15 and my APRS mobile station is WA1LOU-8.

   b. At the ports prompt, type **S** (for single port). If you have a GPS receiver connected to another port, type **D** (for dual ports).

   c. At the TNC COM port prompt, type the number of the computer serial (COM) port that is connected to your TNC, then press **Enter**.

   d. At the TNC baud rate prompt, type the baud rate used for communications between your TNC and the computer serial (COM) port that is connected to your TNC, then press **Enter**.

   e. At the band prompt, select the operating band of the APRS radio equipment. Type either **H** for HF or **V** for VHF or UHF.

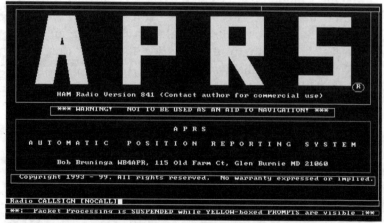

Figure 3-1—The prompts at the bottom of the APRS start-up screen gather information to configure the software.

f. At the type of TNC prompt, select the TNC brand and/or model you are using. The selections are AEA, Dual-Pico (for a dual-port PacComm PicoPacket), KANTRONICS, PacComm (for all other PacComm TNCs), THD7 (for the Kenwood TH-D7 TNC-radio) and OTHER (for everything else). Type the first letter of the TNC type (**A**, **D**, **K**, **P**, **T** or **O**).

g. At the next prompt, indicate whether the TNC you are using is a dual-band Kantronics KAM, AEA PK-900/2232, or neither, by typing **K**, **A**, or **N** respectively.

h. If you typed **S** at the ports prompt (step b), then go to step x. If you have a GPS receiver connected to another COM port and you typed D at the ports prompt, then go to the next step.

i. At the COM port prompt, type the number of the computer serial (COM) port that is connected to your GPS receiver, then press **Enter**.

j. At the type of device prompt, type **G** for GPS receiver.

k. At the device baud rate prompt, type the baud rate used for communications between your GPS receiver and the computer serial (COM) port that is connected to your GPS receiver, then press **Enter**.

l. At the screen refresh rate prompt, indicate how often (in seconds) APRS will refresh its display, then press **Enter**.

m. At the packet transmit rate, indicate how often (in seconds) *APRS* will transmit position packets containing the position information as determined by your GPS receiver, then press **Enter**.

n. At the PC clock prompt, select the time used by the computer clock. Type **Z** for Zulu/Greenwich Mean/ Universal Time or type **L** for local time.

o. At the time zone prompt, type the number of hours (+ or –) your time zone differs from GMT/UTC if your computer clock uses local time, then press **Enter**.

p. At the Daylight Saving prompt, indicate if you are currently using Daylight Saving Time by typing **Y** (for yes) or **N** (for no).

5. After the map of the United States appears, as illustrated in **Figure 3-2**, use the computer mouse or arrow keys to move the cursor to your approximate location on the map. Use the

Page Down key as many times as necessary to magnify the map to permit you to more accurately position the cursor on your location, as illustrated in **Figure 3-3**. When you believe that the cursor is positioned on your location, go to the next step. Note that if there is any APRS activity occurring, APRS stations will start appearing on your map. This is an indication

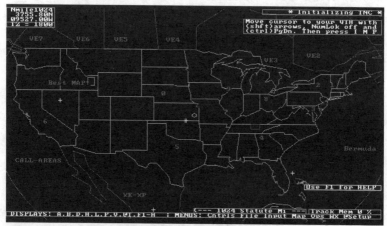

Figure 3-2—When the APRS map of the United States appears, use the computer mouse or arrow keys to move the cursor to your approximate location.

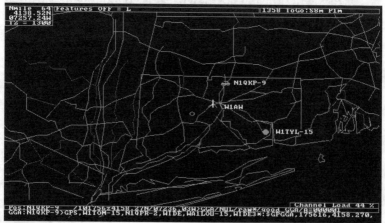

Figure 3-3—The Page Down key magnifies the APRS map to permit you to more accurately position the cursor on your location.

that the installation and configuration of the APRS hardware and software has been successful so far. To refresh the map display, press the **Space Bar** at any time.

6. Type **I** (for Input), then **M** (for My Data), then **P** (for Position).

7. The latitude prompt appears with the latitude calculated from the cursor position on the map. You may accept the calculated latitude by pressing **Enter** or you may refine the latitude by typing it in the following format: DDMM.SSC, where DD is degrees, MM is minutes, SS is seconds and C is direction (N or S). For example, if your latitude is 41° 37' 48" North, type 4137.48N.

8. The longitude prompt appears with the longitude calculated from the cursor position on the map. You may accept the calculated longitude by pressing Enter or you may refine the longitude by typing it in the following format: DDDMM.SSC, where DDD is degrees, MM is minutes, SS is seconds and C is direction (E or W). For example, if your longitude is 72° 56' 43" West, enter 07256.43W.

9. When prompted, select a symbol to represent your station on the map. Refer to **Table 3-1** (at the end of this chapter) for the list of selectable symbols. To select a symbol, type the first letter of the symbol's name (for example, D for Dog). Then, type the number of the symbol you want from the numbered list of symbols that appears (for example, 9 for dog).

10. Assuming your station is located in your home and your home is not moving, ignore the next two prompts concerning course and speed (just press **Enter** in response to each prompt). If your station is mobile and you are not configuring a GPS receiver with APRS, then at the course and speed prompts, type the direction (in degrees) and speed (in mile per hour) that your station is moving. Press **Enter** after each entry.

11. At the comments prompt, you may type a remark that the program appends to each APRS position packet that it transmits. The remark can be related to your name, location, or whatever you feel is appropriate. If you don't know what you want as a comment at this time, you can use the I, M and P commands later to add a comment after you see what other stations on the air are using.

12. At the date-time prompt, press **Enter** if the displayed date

and time (Zulu/Greenwich Mean/Universal Time) are correct. If the date and time are incorrect, type the correct date and time in the following format: DDHHMM, where DD is the day of the month, HH is the hour of the day and MM is the minute of the hour, then press **Enter**.

13. Confirm that the information you entered is correct by typing **Y** (for yes). Your station icon and call sign now appears on the map, as illustrated in **Figure 3-4**.

14. Type **U** (for Unproto).

15. At the new path prompt, type the digipeater path you wish to use, for example, VIA WA1LOU-15,WIDE, then press **Enter**.

16. Type **I** (for Input), then **P** (for Power-Height-Gain).

17. At the power prompt, type your transmitter power in watts, then press **Enter**. The maximum entry in this field is 81 watts. Entering anything larger than 81 results in 81. The purpose of this limitation is to promote the use of minimum power in APRS networks.

18. At the Height Above Average Terrain prompt, type your station's Height Above Average Terrain (HAAT) in feet, then press **Enter**.

19. At the antenna gain prompt, type the station antenna's gain in dB, then press **Enter**.

20. At the direction prompt, type the direction (in degrees) that

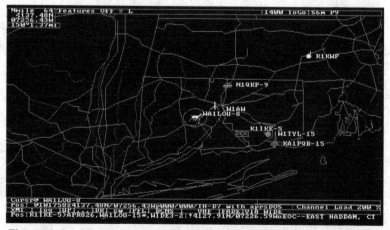

Figure 3-4—After confirming your station information, your station icon and call sign appear on the APRS map.

station antenna favors, then press **Enter**. For North, type 360 degrees and for an omnidirectional antenna, type 0 degrees. If local terrain affects the operation of your omnidirectional antenna, however, you may type a figure that represents the direction that your antenna favors. For example, if a mountain to your west causes your omnidirectional antenna to favor the east, type **90**.

21. Save your APRS configuration by typing **ALT-S** (press the ALT and S keys at the same time), then type **S** again (for Save).

22. At the validation number prompt, type your registration number, then press **Enter**. (Avoiding reconfiguration each time you start *APRS* should be plenty of incentive to register the software.)

23. At the alternate extension prompt, you may type an alternate three-character extension for your *APRS* configuration file name. (You can use an extension switch to select a specific configuration file when you start *APRS* from DOS.) To select the default extension (.APR), just press **Enter**.

That completes the initial installation and configuration of APRS. Once you get a feel for your local APRS network, you can fine tune the configuration especially as it relates to the path your APRS packets use and how your APRS station fits into your local APRS network.

APRS+SA **Installation and Configuration**

APRS+SA is a *Windows* (*95*, *98*, or *NT*) version of APRS written by Brent Hildebrand, KH2Z, that uses *Street Atlas USA* versions 4, 5 and 6 for its maps.

APRS+SA is distributed in two compressed files: *APRSPLUS1.ZIP* and *APRSPLUS2.ZIP*.

To decompress *APRS+SA*, use the shareware application *WinZip*, which is available from **http://www.winzip.com**.

The following procedures describe how to install and configure *APRS+SA*. These procedures assume that you are familiar with the operation of the *Windows*.

1. Power up your computer.
2. Double-click on the *APRSPLUS1.ZIP* icon to start *WinZip*.
3. Select **Extract** from the **Actions** menu.

4. When the Extract window appears, click on the **All Files** and **Use Folder Names** buttons to enable them if they are not already enabled.

5. In the Folders/drives window, select the drive and folder where you wish *WinZip* to store the decompressed *APRS+SA* files.

6. Click on the **Extract** button and *WinZip* decompresses *APRSPLUS1.ZIP*.

7. When decompression is completed, double-click on the *APRSPLUS2.ZIP* icon.

8. Select **Extract** from the **Actions** menu.

9. In the Folders/drives window, click on the **Extract** button and *WinZip* decompresses *APRSPLUS2.ZIP*.

10. When decompression is completed, select **Exit** from the **File** menu.

11. Double-click on the **Setup.exe** application icon in the folder containing the decompressed *APRS+SA* files.

12. When the Setup Complete window appears, click on the **OK** button.

That completes the installation of *APRS+SA*. Now you can configure *APRS+SA* according to the following steps. Remember that if you have not registered *APRS+SA*, you must configure the software each time you start it.

1. Assuming that your computer is already on, power up the rest of your APRS hardware (TNC, radio equipment and GPS receiver, if any).

2. Tune the radio to the local APRS operating frequency (144.39, 445.925 and 10.1515 MHz are the national APRS operating frequencies) and APRS mode (FM on VHF and UHF, LSB on HF).

3. Double-click on the **APRSplus** application icon to start *APRS+SA*.

4. When the *APRS+SA* start-up window appears, click on the **OK** button.

5. When the Unregistered Copy Notification window appears, click on the **OK** button.

6. When the *APRS+SA* main window appears, click on the **Setup** menu.

7. When the *APRS+SA* Setup window appears, as illustrated in

Figure 3-5, configure the following parameters in the Main Parameters tab as required.

a. Callsign—Type your call sign, then press **Tab**. Remember to enter an SSID if one is desired. An SSID (for secondary station identifier) is a number (0-15) that follows a packet radio station call sign (and a hyphen). It is used to differentiate between two or more packet radio stations operating under the same call sign. For example, my APRS digipeater is WA1LOU-15 and my APRS mobile station is WA1LOU-8.

Enter your call sign and SSID.

b. Registration—Type your registration number, then press **Tab**. (Avoiding reconfiguration each time you start *APRS+SA* should be plenty of incentive to register the software.)

c. Click on the **Latitude Longitude** button.

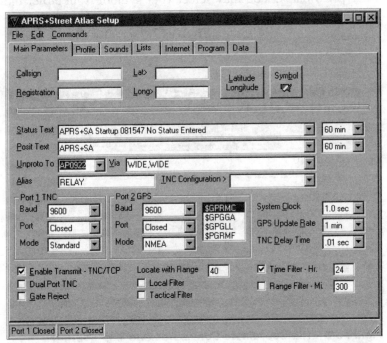

Figure 3-5—You enter the your station information in the fields of the APRS+SA Setup window's Main Parameters tab.

d. When the Coordinate Conversion and Map Capture window appears, as illustrated in **Figure 3-6**, type the latitude (where your APRS station is located) in degrees, minutes and seconds in the **Deg**, **Min** and **Sec** fields, respectively. For southern latitudes, type a minus sign before the degree entry. Press the **Tab** key after each entry.

e. Type the longitude (where your APRS station is located) in degrees, minutes and seconds in the **Deg**, **Min** and **Sec** fields, respectively. For western longitudes, type a minus sign before the degree entry. Press the **Tab** key after each entry.

f. Click on the **OK** button. The Coordinate Conversion and Map Capture window closes and the Lat and Long fields are filled with your APRS station coordinates in the format required by *APRS+SA*.

g. Click on the **Symbol** button.

h. When the Transmitted Symbol window appears, click on the symbol that you wish to represent your station on the APRS maps. You may select your symbol from either the Primary or Secondary Table by clicking on the appropriate tab to view each table. (**Figures 3-7** and **3-8** illustrate each table.)

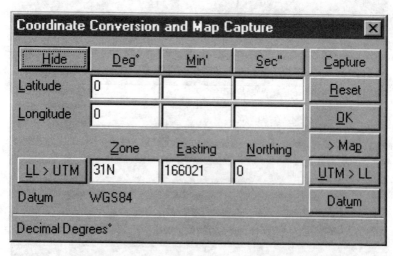

Figure 3-6—The Coordinate Conversion and Map Capture window converts the station coordinates you enter into the APRS+SA format.

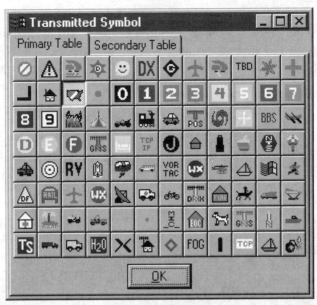

Figure 3-7—The APRS+SA Primary Transmitted Symbol table offers a set of symbols you can select to represent your station on APRS maps.

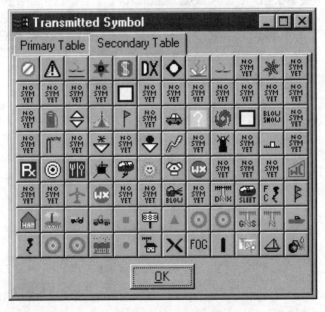

Figure 3-8—The Secondary Transmitted Symbol table of APRS+SA offers additional symbols to represent your station on APRS maps.

i. After you select a symbol, click on the **OK** button. The Transmitted Symbol window closes and the symbol you selected appears on the Symbol button.

j. Status Text—Type a short string of text to be sent whenever *APRS+SA* transmits your station's beacon. Next to this field, set the timer to how often you want *APRS+SA* to transmit a beacon. Stationary stations should use the timer's default setting.

k. Posit Text—Type a short string of text to be sent whenever *APRS+SA* transmits your station's position packet. Next to this field, set the timer to how often you want *APRS+SA* to transmit a position packet. Stationary stations should use the timer's default setting.

l. Alias—Type the alias for your APRS station. Use the default (RELAY) unless your station is a digipeater or gateway.

m. Via—Type the desired digipeater path or select one from the scrolling list (RELAY,WIDE; ECHO; ECHO,GATE; WIDE or WIDE,WIDE).

n. TNC Configuration—From the scrolling list, select the model of TNC you will use with *APRS+SA*. Select dsp2232.tnc for the AEA DSP-2232, pk-232.tnc for the AEA/Time Wave PK-232, initaea.tnc for all other AEA TNCs, initkam.tnc for the Kantronics KAM, initkpc3.tnc for the Kantronics KPC-3, inittapr.tnc for TNCs compatible with the TAPR TNC-2, or InitVHF for all other TNCs that will operate on VHF. When in doubt, select inittapr.tnc or InitVHF.

o. Port 1 TNC baud—From the scrolling list, select the data rate (1200, 2400, 4800, 9600, or 19200) used for communications between your computer and TNC.

p. Port 1 TNC port—From the scrolling list, select the number of the computer serial (COM) port (1-10) that is connected to your TNC.

q. Port 1 TNC mode—From the scrolling list, select your TNC - GPS receiver configuration. Select Pico if the configuration uses a dual-port PacComm Pico-Packet or HSP is the configuration uses a hardware single port switch. Otherwise, select StandaRd.

r. If you will not be using a GPS receiver with *APRS+SA*, then go to step v.

s. Port 2 GPS baud—From the scrolling list, select the data

rate (1200, 2400, 4800, or 9600) used for communications between your computer and GPS receiver.

t. Port 2 GPS port—From the scrolling list, select the number of the computer serial (COM) port (1-10) that is connected to your GPS receiver. Select Closed if the second serial (COM) port is not connected to a GPS receiver.

u. Port 2 GPS mode—From the scrolling lists, select the mode used by your GPS receiver: (NMEA, Tripmate, Garmin) and the GPS sentence ($GPRMC, $GPGGA, $GPGLL, $PGRMF, $LCGLL, $LCBWC) *APRS+SA* uses to determine your position for position packet transmissions.

v. Enable Transmit—Click in this check box (if a check mark does not already appear in this box) to cause APRS+SA to initialize the TNC and begin transmitting APRS packets.

8. Click on the **Profile** tab. When the Profile tab of the *APRS+SA* Setup window appears, as illustrated in **Figure 3-9**, configure the following parameters as required.

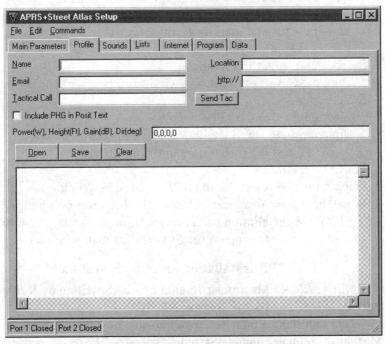

Figure 3-9—Use the Profile tab of the APRS+SA Setup window to delineate the RF capabilities of your station.

a. Power(W), Height(Ft), Gain(dB), Dir(Deg)—Power—Type your transmitter power in watts, your station's Height Above Average Terrain (HAAT) in feet, your station antenna's gain in dB, and the direction (in degrees) that station antenna favors. Separate each entry with a comma, but no spaces. Note that the maximum meaningful entry in the Power field is 81 watts. If you enter anything larger than 81, *APRS+SA* still calculates your station's coverage area as if its transmitter power was 81 watts. The purpose of this limitation is to promote the use of minimum power in APRS networks. In the Dir field, type 360 degrees for North and 0 degrees for an omnidirectional antenna, however, if local terrain effects the operation of your omnidirectional antenna, you may type a figure that represents the direction that your antenna favors. For example, if a mountain to your west causes your omnidirectional antenna to favor the east, type 90.

b. Include PHG in Posit Text—Click this check box (if a check mark does not already appear in this box) to cause *APRS+SA* to transmit the transmitter power, HAAT, antenna gain and directivity information in each position packet that it transmits.

9. Select **Save** from the **File** menu.
10. When the Save Setup File As window appears, click on the **Save** button.
11. Select **Close** from the **File** menu.

This completes the installation and basic configuration of *APRS+SA*. To test the installation and configuration:

1. Start *Street Atlas*.
2. Click on the **Maps** tab in the *APRS+SA* main window.
3. When the **Maps** tab appears, click on the **1 All Reports** button.
4. If *APRS+SA* installation and configuration is correct, stations should begin appearing on the *Street Atlas* map window.

MacAPRS Installation and Configuration

MacAPRS is a Macintosh version of APRS written by Keith Sproul, WU2Z, and Mark Sproul, KB2ICI.

The minimum computer requirements of *MacAPRS* are a Macintosh computer running System 7.0 or later. The recommended computer configuration is a color Macintosh with 8 Mbytes of RAM.

MacAPRS is distributed as a compressed file, *MacAPRS_###_ppc.sit*, where *###* is the version number of the software, for example, *MacAPRS_327_ppc.sit*. Besides the *MacAPRS* application, this compressed file also contains documentation and a sufficient sampling of maps to get you up and running.

To decompress *MacAPRS*, use the shareware application *StuffIT Expander*, which is available from **http://www.Aladdinsys.com**.

The following procedures describe how to install and configure MacAPRS. These procedures assume that you are familiar with the operation of the Macintosh operating system.

1. Power up your computer.
2. Drag the compressed *MacAPRS* file icon on top of the *StuffIT Expander* icon and *StuffIT Expander* decompresses the files.

That completes the installation of *MacAPRS*. Now you can configure *MacAPRS* according to the following steps. Remember that if you have not registered *MacAPRS*, you must configure the software each time you start it.

1. Assuming that your computer is already on, power up the rest of your APRS hardware (TNC, radio equipment and GPS

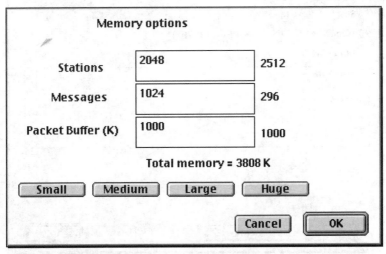

Figure 3-10—The MacAPRS Memory Options window allows you to allocate computer memory according to your expectations regarding APRS activity.

receiver, if any).

2. Tune the radio to the local APRS operating frequency (144.39, 445.925 and 10.1515 MHz are the national APRS operating frequencies) and APRS mode (FM on VHF and UHF, LSB on HF).

3. Double-click on the *MacAPRS* application icon to start *MacAPRS*.

4. When the *MacAPRS* Memory Options window appears, as illustrated in **Figure 3-10**, select the desired memory setting (small, medium, large, or huge, which equates to 1455, 1654, 3808 and 3808 kbytes of RAM, respectively), then click on the **OK** button.

5. When the TNC Configuration and Type window appears, as illustrated in **Figure 3-11**, click on the button that represents your TNC configuration (one TNC on VHF or HF, two TNCs, or a dual-port TNC), then click on the **OK** button.

6. When the *MacAPRS* main window appears, select **Station Settings...** from the **Settings** menu.

7. When the *MacAPRS* Station Settings window appears, as

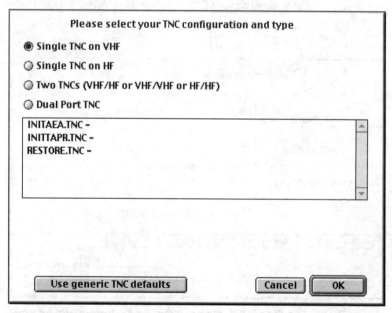

Figure 3-11—Select your TNC setup from the MacAPRS TNC Configuration and Type window.

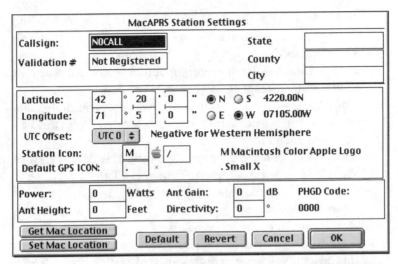

Figure 3-12—You enter most of the information concerning your station in the MacAPRS Station Settings window.

illustrated in **Figure 3-12**, configure its parameter as required.

a. Callsign—Type your call sign, then press **Tab**. Remember to enter an SSID if one is desired. An SSID (for secondary station identifier) is a number (0-15) that follows a packet radio station call sign (and a hyphen). It is used to differentiate between two or more packet radio stations operating under the same call sign. For example, my APRS digipeater is WA1LOU-15 and my APRS mobile station is WA1LOU-8.

Enter your call sign and SSID.

b. Validation #—Type your registration number, then press **Tab**. (Avoiding reconfiguration each time you start *MacAPRS* should be plenty of incentive to register the software.)

c. State—Type the two-letter abbreviation for the state or province where your APRS station is located, then press **Tab**.

d. County—Type the name of the county where your APRS station is located, then press **Tab**.

e. City—Type the name of the town or city where your APRS station is located, then press **Tab**.

f. Latitude—Type the latitude (in degrees, minutes and seconds) where your APRS station is located. Press the **Tab** key after each entry.

g. N / S—Click on the appropriate button **N** or **S** for North or South latitude respectively, then press **Tab**.

h. Longitude—Type the longitude (in degrees, minutes and seconds) where your APRS station is located. Press the **Tab** key after each entry.

i. E / W—Click on the appropriate button **E** or **W** for East or West longitude respectively, then press **Tab**.

j. UTC Offset—From this menu, select the number of hours (+ or –) your local time differs from Greenwich Mean/ Universal Time, then press **Tab**.

k. Station Icon—Type the alphanumeric character that stands for the icon you wish to represent your station on the APRS maps (for example, p for puppy), then press **Tab**. Refer to Table 3-1 for the list of selectable symbols.

l. Default GPS ICON—Leave this parameter at its default setting by pressing **Tab**.

m. Power—Type your transmitter power in watts, then press Tab. The maximum meaningful entry in this field is 81 watts. If you enter anything larger than 81, *MacAPRS* still calculates your station's coverage area as if its transmitter power was 81 watts. The purpose of this limitation is to promote the use of minimum power in APRS networks.

n. Ant Height—Type your station's Height Above Average Terrain (HAAT) in feet, then press **Tab**.

o. Ant Gain—Type the station antenna's gain in dB, then press **Enter**.

p. Directivity—Type the direction (in degrees) that station antenna favors. For North, type 360 degrees and for an omnidirectional antenna, type 0 degrees, however, if local terrain effects the operation of your omnidirectional antenna, you may type a figure that represents the direction that your antenna favors. For example, if a mountain to your west causes your omnidirectional antenna to favor the east, type 90.

q. When you are finished configuring the parameters in the Station Settings window, click on the **OK** button.

8. The icon you selected in step 7k now appears on the map at

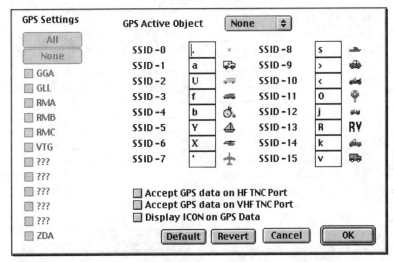

Figure 3-13—Use the GPS Settings window to configure MacAPRS for operation with a GPS receiver.

the longitude and latitude you entered.

9. If you will not be using a GPS receiver with *MacAPRS*, go to step 12.

10. If you will be using a GPS receiver with *MacAPRS*, select **GPS Settings...** from the **Settings** menu.

11. When the GPS Settings window appears, as illustrated in **Figure 3-13**, select **Accept GPS data on VHF TNC Port** or **Accept GPS data on HF TNC Port** depending on your TNC configuration, then click on the OK button.

12. Select TNC **Settings...** from the **Settings** menu.

13. When the *MacAPRS* TNC Settings window appears, as illustrated in **Figure 3-14**, configure the following parameters as required.

    a. In the Unproto APRSM Via field, type the digipeater path you wish to use, for example, VIA WA1LOU-15,WIDE.

    b. On the left side of the window, select your TNC Type
       Receive Only—Click on this button if your configuration is for receiving APRS only.

       Single Port—Click on this button if your TNC has one radio port (HF or VHF).

       Dual Port—Click on this button if your TNC has separate HF

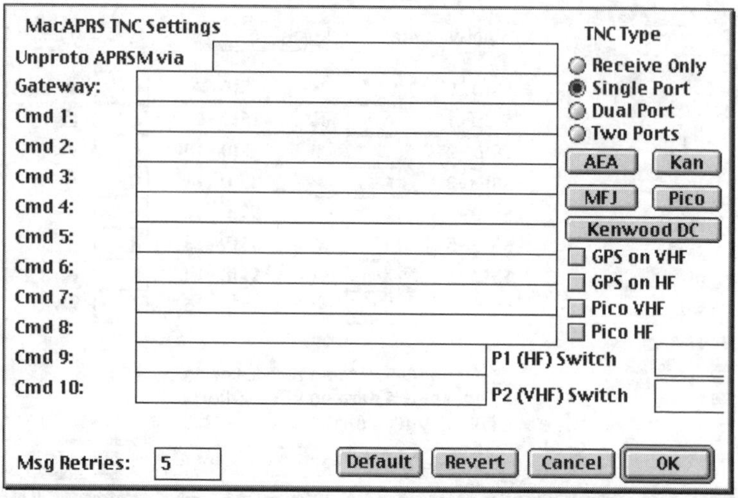

```
MacAPRS TNC Settings                                    TNC Type
Unproto APRSM via  [                    ]               ○ Receive Only
Gateway:           [                    ]               ● Single Port
Cmd 1:             [                    ]               ○ Dual Port
Cmd 2:             [                    ]               ○ Two Ports
Cmd 3:             [                    ]               [ AEA ]  [ Kan ]
Cmd 4:             [                    ]               [ MFJ ]  [ Pico ]
Cmd 5:             [                    ]               [ Kenwood DC ]
Cmd 6:             [                    ]               ☐ GPS on VHF
Cmd 7:             [                    ]               ☐ GPS on HF
Cmd 8:             [                    ]               ☐ Pico VHF
Cmd 9:             [                    ]               ☐ Pico HF
Cmd 10:            [                    ]    P1 (HF) Switch  [      ]
                                             P2 (VHF) Switch [      ]

Msg Retries:  [ 5 ]          [ Default ] [ Revert ] [ Cancel ] [ OK ]
```

Figure 3-14—The TNC Settings window fine-tunes MacAPRS for compatibility with your TNC brand, model and configuration.

and VHF radio ports.

Two Ports—Click on this button if your TNC has two VHF radio ports.

c. Click on the appropriate button for your brand of TNC: **AEA**, **Kan** (for Kantronics), **MFJ**, **Pico** (for PacComm PicoPacket), or **Kenwood DC** (for the Kenwood TH-D7 transceiver). (After clicking on a button, the appropriate commands for that TNC are loaded into the command fields of the *MacAPRS* TNC Settings window.)

d. If your TNC is a PacComm PicoPacket with two serial ports and a GPS receiver is connected to one of the ports, click **Pico VHF** if the GPS receiver is connected to the VHF port or **Pico HF** if the GPS receiver is connected to the HF port.

e. If your TNC is a KPC-3+ with version 3.8 (or later) firmware and a GPS receiver is connected to the radio port of the TNC, then enter the following commands in any empty Cmd fields:

> **GPSHEAD 1 $GPRMC**
> **LTP 1 GPS VIA (your digipeater path)**
> **BLT 1 EVERY 00:10:00 CLEAR**
> **LTRACK 5 LT1 TIME**
> **GPSTIME VALID RMC**

GPSPORT 4800 NORMAL CHECKSUM

14. When you are finished configuring the parameters in the *MacAPRS* TNC Settings window, click on the **OK** button.
15. Select ***MacAPRS Settings...*** from the **Settings** menu.
16. When the *MacAPRS* Settings window appears, as illustrated in **Figure 3-15**, configure the following parameters as required.
    a. In the Status Text field, you may type a remark that the program appends to each APRS position packet that it transmits. The remark can be related to your name, location, or whatever you feel is appropriate. If you don't know what you want as a comment at this time, you can access the *MacAPRS* Settings window later to add a comment after you see what other stations on the air are using.
    b. In the Automatic Input panel, select either **VHF TNC** or **HF (Dual) TNC**, depending on your TNC configuration. If a GPS receiver is connected to your TNC, also select **GPS/NMEA**.
17. Click on the **OK** button to close the *MacAPRS* Settings window.
18. Select **Communications...** from the **Settings** menu, then

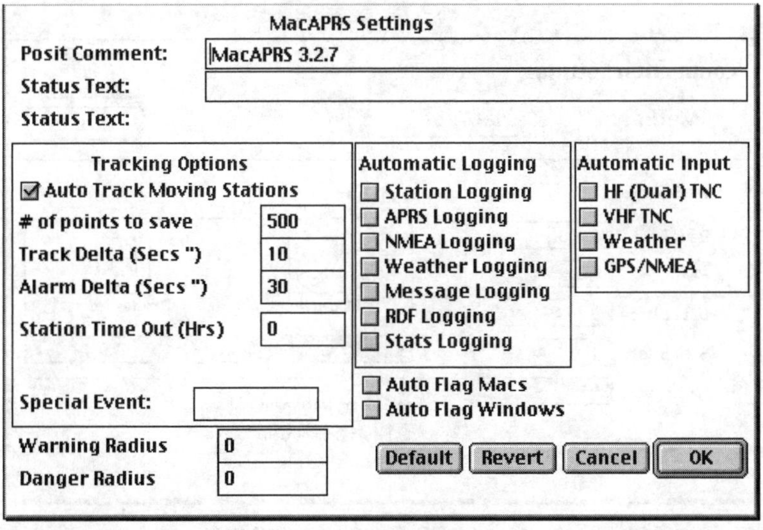

Figure 3-15—Enter your station's status text in the MacAPRS Settings window.

select **HF (or Dual Port) TNC** or **VHF TNC** from the **Communications...** sub-menu depending on your TNC configuration.

19. When the Connection Settings window appears, as illustrated in **Figure 3-16**, select the following parameters to conform with the parameters used for communications between your TNC and the computer serial port that is connected to your TNC.

   a. Method—Select the extension (Serial Tool or TCE TCP Tool) used by the Macintosh operating system for managing the computer's serial ports.

   b. Baud Rate—From the scrolling list, select the data rate used for communications between your TNC and computer.

   c. Parity—From the scrolling list, select the method of checking the accuracy of a received character by adding an extra bit in order that the character will have an even or odd number of one bits depending on the type of parity used (even, odd, or none).

   d. Data Bits—From the scrolling list, select the number of bits (5, 6, 7 or 8) that represent an alphanumeric or control character used in communications between your TNC and computer.

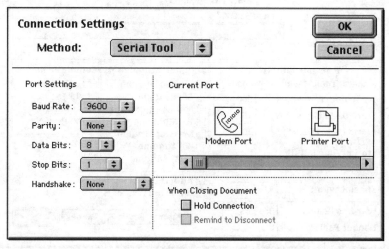

Figure 3-16—In the MacAPRS Connection Settings window, you select parameters for communications between your computer and the TNC and GPS receiver connected to it.

e. Stop Bits—From the scrolling list, select the number of bits (1, 1.5 or 2) that follow a character (to indicate its end) used in communications between your TNC and computer.

f. Handshake—From the scrolling list, select the protocol used for coordinating communications between your TNC and computer. The choices are None, XON/XOFF, DTR & CTS, DTR only, and CTS only. When in doubt, select None.

g. Current Port—From the scrolling list, select the computer serial port (Modem Port or Printer Port) that is connected to your TNC.

20. When you are finished configuring the parameters in the Connections Settings window, click on the **OK** button.

21. If no GPS receiver is connected to a serial port of your computer, go to step 25.

22. If a GPS receiver is connected to a serial port of your computer, select **Communications...** from the **Settings** menu, then select **NMEA/GPS** from the sub-menu.

23. When the Connection Settings window appears, as illustrated in Figure 3-16, select the following parameters to conform with the parameters used for communications between your GPS receiver and the computer serial port that is connected to your GPS receiver.

a. Method—Select the extension (Serial Tool or TCE TCP Tool) used by the Macintosh operating system for managing the computer's serial ports.

b. Baud Rate—From the scrolling list, select the data rate used for communications between your GPS receiver and computer.

c. Parity—From the scrolling list, select the method of checking the accuracy of a received character by adding an extra bit in order that the character will have an even or odd number of one bits depending on the type of parity used (even, odd, or none).

d. Data Bits—From the scrolling list, select the number of bits (5, 6, 7 or 8) that represent an alphanumeric or control character used in communications between your GPS receiver and computer.

e. Stop Bits—From the scrolling list, select the number of bits (1, 1.5 or 2) that follow a character (to indicate its end) used in communications between your GPS receiver and computer.

f. Handshake—From the scrolling list, select the protocol used for coordinating communications between your GPS receiver and computer. The choices are None, XON/XOFF, DTR & CTS, DTR only, and CTS only. When in doubt, select None.

g. Current Port—From the scrolling list, select the computer serial port (Modem Port or Printer Port) that is connected to your GPS receiver.

24. When you are finished configuring the parameters in the Connections Settings window, click on the **OK** button.

25. Select **Open HF TNC (Dual Port)** or **Open VHF TNC** from the **Settings** menu depending on your TNC configuration.

26. If a GPS receiver is connected to a serial port of your computer, select **Open GPS/NMEA** from the **Settings** menu.

This completes the installation and basic configuration of *MacAPRS*. If *MacAPRS* successfully initialized the TNC connected to your computer and the radio connected to the TNC is tuned to an active APRS channel, stations should begin appearing on the *MacAPRS* map window.

pocketAPRS Installation and Configuration

pocketAPRS is a version of APRS written by Mike Musick, NØQBF, that runs on a 3Com Palm III Connected Organizer, which is a hand-held personal digital assistant (PDA).

pocketAPRS is distributed as a compressed file, *paprs###.zip*, where *###* is the version number of the software, for example, *paprs100.zip*. Besides the *pocketAPRS* application, this compressed file also contains documentation, but no maps. The *pocketAPRS* maps are distributed as separate compressed files.

To decompress *pocketAPRS* on a Macintosh computer, use the shareware application *ZipIt*, which is available from **http://www.maczipit.com**. To decompress *pocketAPRS* on a computer running *Windows 95*, *97* or *NT*, use the shareware application *WinZip*, which is available from **http://www.winzip.com**.

The following steps describe how to install and configure *pocketAPRS*. These steps assume that you are familiar with the operation of the Palm III.

Power up your Macintosh or *Windows* computer.

2. For Macintosh:

   a. Double-click on the compressed *pocketAPRS* file icon.

   b. Select **Select All** from the **Edit** menu of ZipIt.

   c. Select **Extract...** from the **Zip** menu.

   d. When the Save File As... window appears, select the drive and folder where you want ZipIt to store the decompressed *pocketAPRS* files, then click on the **Save** button.

   e. Repeat steps a through d for any compressed *pocketAPRS* map files.

   f. When decompression is completed, select **Quit** from the **File** menu.

4. For *Windows*:

   a. Double-click on the compressed *pocketAPRS* file icon.

   b. Select **Extract** from the **Actions** menu of *WinZip*.

   c. When the Extract window appears, click on the **All Files** and **Use Folder Names** buttons to enable them if they are not already enabled.

   d. In the Folders/drives window, select the drive and folder where you wish *WinZip* to store the decompressed *pocketAPRS* files.

   e. Click on the **Extract** button and *WinZip* decompresses the *pocketAPRS* files.

   f. Repeat steps a through e for any compressed *pocketAPRS* map files.

   g. When decompression is completed, select **Exit** from the **File** menu.

5. HotSync the *pocketAPRS* application to your Palm III.

6. HotSync one or more *pocketAPRS* maps to your Palm III. Note that the memory limitations of the Palm III permit storage of only two or three maps.

That completes the installation of *pocketAPRS*. Now you can configure *pocketAPRS* according to the following steps. Remember that if you have not registered *pocketAPRS*, you must configure the software each time you start it.

1. Assuming that your Palm III is already on, power up the rest of your APRS hardware (TNC, radio equipment and GPS receiver, if any).

2. Tune the radio to the local APRS operating frequency (144.39, 445.925 and 10.1515 MHz are the national APRS operating frequencies) and APRS mode (FM on VHF and UHF, LSB on HF).
3. Tap the **APPLICATIONS** icon on the Palm III.
4. Tap the *pocketAPRS* icon.

When the *pocketAPRS* start-up window appears, as illustrated in **Figure 3-17**, tap the **Register** button.

When the Registration window appears, enter your call sign and registration number in the appropriate fields, then tap the **OK** button. (Avoiding reconfiguration each time you start *pocketAPRS* should be plenty of incentive to register the software.)

When the *pocketAPRS* start-up window reappears, tap the **Settings** button.

Figure 3-17—You enter your call sign and registration number in the Registration window of pocketAPRS.

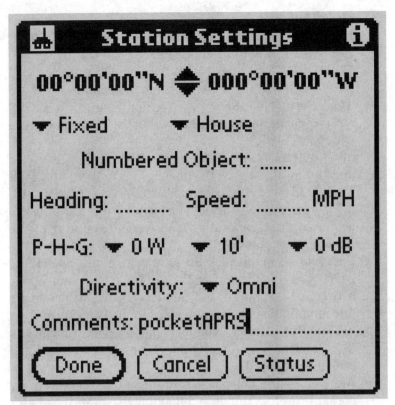

Figure 3-18—You delineate the location and RF capabilities of your station and select its map icon in the pocketAPRS Station Settings window.

When the *pocketAPRS* Settings window appears, as illustrated in **Figure 3-18**, configure its parameters as required.

a. Callsign—Enter your call sign. Remember to enter an SSID if one is desired. An SSID (for secondary station identifier) is a number (0-15) that follows a packet radio station call sign (and a hyphen). It is used to differentiate between two or more packet radio stations operating under the same call sign. For example, my APRS digipeater is WA1LOU-15 and my APRS mobile station is WA1LOU-8.

Enter your call sign and SSID.

b. UTC Offset—Tap this pick list to select the number of hours (+ or –) your local time differs from Greenwich

Mean/Universal Time.

c. TNC Type—Tap this pick list to select the model of TNC you will use with *pocketAPRS*: PicoPacket, KPC-3, TH-D7A/E, Tiny-2, or (None) for a non-TNC device, like a GPS, or if nothing is connected to the Palm III.

d. Dual Port TNC—Select this option if there is a GPS receiver connected to the other port of the TNC you will use with pocketAPRS.

e. GPS—Select this option if there is a GPS receiver connected directly to the Palm III running *pocketAPRS* or to a TH-D7A/E transceiver connected to the *pocketAPRS* Palm III.

f. DFjr/microFinder—Select this option if there is an automatic direction finding device connected to the Palm III running *pocketAPRS*.

g. Data rate—Tap this pick list to select the data rate (1200, 2400, 4800, 9600, or 19.2k) used for communications between the Palm III and the TNC, GPS, or automatic direction finding device connected to the Palm III running *pocketAPRS*. Other communication port parameters (8 character bits, no parity and 1 stop bit) are fixed and cannot be changed.

h. Arc Units—Tap this pick list to select the format used by *pocketAPRS* for latitude and longitude DD° MM' SS" (for degrees, minutes and seconds) or DD° MM.mm' (for degrees, minutes and hundredths of minutes).

When you are finished configuring the parameters in the *pocketAPRS* Settings window, tap the **Done** button.

If a TNC is connected to the Palm III, *pocketAPRS* attempts to initialize the TNC with the parameters entered in the *pocketAPRS* Settings window.

If *pocketAPRS* is unable to initialize the TNC, it displays a message indicating such and prompts you to try again. Tap the **Try Again** button.

If the second attempt to initialize the TNC fails, there is a problem in the connection between the Palm III and the TNC. Perhaps there is a wiring problem or the TNC is not configured properly (its data rate must match the data rate you selected in the *pocketAPRS* window).

When the Station Settings window appears, as illustrated in

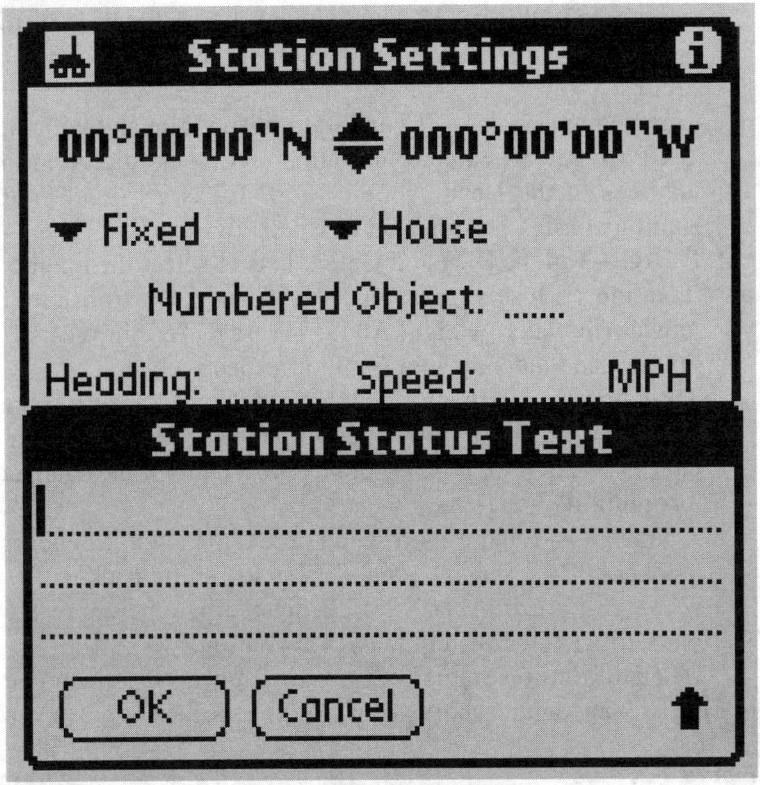

Figure 3-19—In the Station Status Text window, enter a short string of text to be sent as a beacon by pocketAPRS.

Figure 3-19, configure its parameter as required.

   a. Latitude and Longitude—Enter the latitude and longitude of your station location. Tap on the item (degrees, minutes, seconds, compass direction) you wish to enter, then tap on the up and down arrows until the correct value appears. If a GPS receiver is connected, you may skip this step because the GPS receiver provides the coordinates automatically.

   b. Fixed—Tap the first pick list below the Latitude field to select the type of icon that *pocketAPRS* uses to represent your station. The types are Mobile, Fixed, Weather, Event, Numbered, APRS, Ham Radio and Other.

   c. House—Tap the second pick list below the Latitude field to select the specific icon that *pocketAPRS* uses to represent your station.

d. Numbered Object—If you selected a Numbered icon to represent your station, enter the number for that icon in this field.

e. Heading and Speed—If your station is mobile and without a GPS receiver, enter your station's compass direction in degrees in the Heading field (360° for North) and your station's miles-per-hour in the Speed field.

f. P-H-G—Tap the **P**, **H** and **G** pick lists to select the number that most closely represents your station's transmitter power (in watts), Height Above Average Terrain (HAAT, in feet) and antenna gain (in dB), respectively.

g. Directivity—Tap the this pick list to select the approximate compass direction your station's antenna favors, that is, NE, E, SE, S, SW, W, NW, or N. Select Omni if the antenna is omnidirectional.

h. Comments—Enter a short string of text to be sent whenever pocketAPRS transmits your station's position packet.

When you are finished configuring the parameters in the Station Settings window, tap the **Status** button.

When the Station Status Text window appears, as illustrated in **Figure 3-20**, enter a short string of text to be sent as a beacon.

Figure 3-20—Use the Transmit Control window to determine how pocketAPRS sends APRS packets.

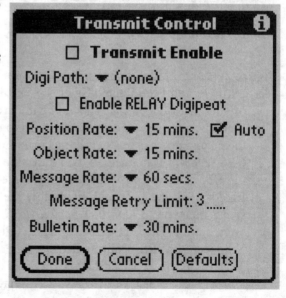

When you are finished entering text in the Station Status Text window, tap the **OK** button.

When the Station Settings window appears, tap the **Done** button.

When the Station List window appears, tap the **MENU** button.

Select **Transmit Control** from the **Settings** menu.

When the Transmit Control window appears, as illustrated in Figure 3-20, configure its parameters as required.

a. Transmit Enable—Select this option to allow *pocketAPRS* to transmit.

b. Digi Path—Tap this pick list to choose the desired digipeater path from the following selections: (none); RELAY,WIDE; WIDE,WIDE; RELAY,WIDE,WIDE. Select Add/Edit Paths... to create and save unique digipeater paths.

c. Enable RELAY Digipeat—Select this option to allow pocketAPRS to function as a RELAY digipeater.

d. Position, Object, Message and Bulletin Rate—Tap these pick lists to select how often *pocketAPRS* transmits position, object, message and bulletin packets, respectively.

e. Auto—Select this option to allow *pocketAPRS* to transmit a position packet after you have moved one mile from where it had transmitted the previous position packet. This option overrides the Position Rate option. If you have stopped long enough for *pocketAPRS* to send a position packet based on the Position Rate timer selection, Auto causes *pocketAPRS* to send another position packet after moving approximately 0.1 miles.

f. Message Retry Limit—Tap this pick list to select the maximum number of times *pocketAPRS* retransmits an unacknowledged message packet.

g. Bulletin Rate—Tap this pick list to how often *pocketAPRS* retransmits a bulletin packet.

When you are finished configuring the parameters in the Transmit Control window, tap the **Done** button (and the Station List window appears).

This completes the installation and basic configuration of *pocketAPRS*. If *pocketAPRS* successfully initialized the TNC connected to the Palm III and the radio connected to the TNC is tuned to an active APRS channel, entries should begin appearing in the Station List window.

TH-D7

[*Note:* As this is written, Kenwood is about to release its new TM-D700 mobile transceiver. Its APRS capabilities are expected to be similar to the TH-D7 hand-held transceiver. The text that follows refers only to the TH-D7, but much of it will also apply to the TM-D700.]

The Kenwood TH-D7 dual-band transceiver may be used for APRS in two ways. It may be used as a standalone APRS station by means of its built-in APRS software. Also, it may be used as the radio and TNC portion of an APRS station by configuring its built-in TNC using any of the versions of APRS described above.

CONFIGURING TH-D7 APRS SOFTWARE

The APRS software built into the TH-D7 may be configured to provide you with a complete handheld APRS station. There are two ways to configure the TH-D7 software: by means of the front panel of the TH-D7 or by means of Kenwood's optional MCP-D7 software for *Windows 95/98*.

Front Panel Configuration

To configure TH-D7 using its front panel...

1. Press the **POWER** button to power the TH-D7.
2. Press the **TNC** button as many times as necessary (once or twice) until the transceiver displays [TNC___] *not* followed by the word PACKET.
3. Press the **MENU** button, then press **1**, **4** and **1**.
4. At the DATA BAND prompt, press the **OK** button, then the **up** and **down** buttons to select which band (**A** or **B**) will be used for packet radio. After making your selection, press the **OK** button again.
5. Press the **MENU** button, then tune the radio to the local APRS operating frequency (144.39 and 445.925 are the national APRS operating frequencies).
6. Press the **MENU** button, then press **2** and **1**.
7. At the MY CALL prompt, press the **OK** button, then enter your call sign using the transceiver front panel buttons. After

making your selection, press the **OK** button again. Remember to enter an SSID if one is desired. An SSID (for secondary station identifier) is a number (0-15) that follows a packet radio station call sign (and a hyphen). It is used to differentiate between two or more packet radio stations operating under the same call sign. For example, my APRS digipeater is WA1LOU-15 and my APRS mobile station is WA1LOU-8. Enter your call sign and SSID.

8. Press the **up** button.

9. At the GPS UNIT prompt, press the **OK** button, then press the up and down buttons to select **NMEA** if there is an NMEA-compatible GPS receiver connected to the transceiver or **NOT USED** if there is no GPS receiver connected. After making your selection, press the **OK** button, then the **up** button.

10. If a GPS receiver is connected to the transceiver, go to the next. If a GPS receiver is not connected to the transceiver, at the **MY POSITION** prompt, press the **OK** button, then enter the latitude and longitude of your station location. For latitude, press the **up** and **down** buttons to select **N** or **S** (for North or South latitude respectively), then press the **OK** button. Press the up and down buttons to enter the latitude in the degrees, minutes and hundredths of minutes fields (press the **OK** button in between fields). For longitude, press the **up** and **down** buttons to select **E** or **W** (for East or West longitude respectively), then press the **OK** button. Press the **up** and **down** buttons to enter the longitude in the degrees, minutes and hundredths of minutes fields (press the **OK** button in between fields). After making your selection, press the **OK** button again.

11. Press the **up** button.

12. At the POS COMMENT prompt, press the **OK** button, then press the **up** and **down** buttons to select one of eight standard strings of text to be sent whenever the transceiver transmits your station's position packet. The selections are Off Duty, En Route, In Service, Returning, Committed, Special, Priority and Emergency. Selecting Special or Priority causes your station to be highlighted on the computer displays of other APRS stations that receive your packet. Selecting Emergency sets off alarms in the computers of other APRS stations that receive your packet, so this comment should only be selected

if there actually is an emergency. After making your selection, press the **OK** button, then the **up** button.

13. At the ICON prompt, press the **OK** button, then press the **up** and **down** buttons to select the icon you wish to represent your station on the APRS maps. You may choose one of the 15 icons that the transceiver can display or you may choose an icon that the transceiver cannot display by selecting **OTHERS**, then press the **OK** button. At the SYMBOL prompt, press the **up** and **down** buttons to select the alphanumeric character that represents the icon you wish to use, then press the **OK** button. At the TABLE prompt, press the **up** and **down** buttons to select the icon table (/ or \) from which you select the icon. After making your selection, press the **OK** button, then the **up** button.

14. At the STATUS TEXT prompt, press the **OK** button, then use the transceiver front panel buttons to enter a short string of text to be sent whenever the transceiver APRS software transmits your station's position packet. (Entering a 20-character STATUS field almost doubles the length of your packets.) After making your selection, press the **OK** button, then the **up** button.

15. At the TX INTERVAL prompt, press the **OK** button, then press the **up** and **down** buttons to select how often the TH-D7 transmits position packets (every 0.5, 1, 2, 3, 5, 10, 20, or 30 minutes). After making your selection, press the **OK** button, then the **up** button.

16. At the PACKET PATH prompt, press the **OK** button, then use the transceiver front panel buttons to enter the digipeater path you wish to use, for example, VIA WA1LOU-15,WIDE. After making your selection, press the **OK** button, then the **up** button.

17. At the DATA TX prompt, press the **OK** button, then press the **up** and **down** buttons to select either **MANUAL**, **PTT**, or **AUTO** to determine how the transceiver sends position packets. If you select MANUAL, position packets are transmitted each time you press the BCON button on the transceiver. If you select PTT, position packets are transmitted each time you release the PTT switch on the transceiver. If you select AUTO, position packets are transmitted according to the setting of the TX INTERVAL parameter (from 30-second 5 to 30-minute intervals). Note that to enable the PTT and AUTO selections, press the BCON button

to cause the transceiver to display **BCON**. After making your selection, press the **OK** button, then the **up** button.

18. At the UNPROTOCOL prompt, press the **up** button if APK001 is already selected. If not, press the **OK** button, then press the **up** and **down** buttons to select APK001. After selecting APK001, press the **OK** button, then the **up** button.

19. At the POS LIMIT prompt, press the **OK** button, then press the **up** and **down** buttons to select **OFF** to disable the position limit feature or **10** to **2500** miles/kilometers (in 10-mile/kilometer steps) to enable this feature. When enabled, position limit causes the transceiver to ignore packets received from stations beyond the selected distance. After making your selection, press the **OK** button, then the **up** button.

20. At the UNIT prompt, press the **OK** button, then press the **up** and **down** buttons to select **mile,°F** or **km,°C** to determine how the transceiver displays distance and temperature (in miles and degrees Fahrenheit or kilometers and degrees Celsius respectively). After making your selection, press the **OK** button, then the **MENU** button.

21. Select the desired transmit power by pressing the **F** and **MENU** keys until the transceiver displays EL (for extremely low power; L indicates low power and H indicates high power).

22. If a GPS receiver is connected to the transceiver, power it, then press the **POS** button. When the transceiver begins receiving position information from the GPS receiver, the display begins blinking, then it displays the grid square, latitude and longitude.

23. If you selected AUTO or MANUAL in the DATA TX option, press the **BCON** button to cause the transceiver to display BCON. If you selected PTT, depress and release the PTT switch momentarily.

Step 23 causes the transceiver to transmit an APRS position packet (the red LED on the top of the transceiver turns on during a transmission). If the transceiver receives your packet as digipeated, the transceiver displays MY PACKET. This is a sure sign that you have configured the transceiver correctly. If the transceiver does not display MY PACKET, you may have to configure its PACKET PATH parameter differently or increase its transmit power.

If the red LED did not turn on to indicate a transmission, check that the transceiver's transmitter is not inhibited. Press the **MENU** button, then press **1**, **5** and **5** again and check that TX

INHIBIT is set to OFF. If it is set to ON, press the **OK** button, then press the **up** or **down** button to select **OFF**, then press the **OK** button again.

MCP-D7 CONFIGURATION

MCP-D7 is *Windows* software that is available on the optional *Kenwood TH-D7 In-Depth Manual* CD-ROM. **MCP-D7** requires *Windows 95/98*, 1 Mbyte of space on your hard disk for its installation, and 5 Mbytes of RAM to run it. I have also successfully used it on a *Windows NT* computer and a Macintosh computer running *Windows* emulation software (*SoftWindows*).

The following procedures describe how to install *MCP-D7* and how to use *MCP-D7* to configure the APRS software built into the TH-D7. These procedures assume that you are familiar with the operation of *Windows*.

1. Power up your computer.
2. Double-click on the *MCP-D7* **Setup.exe** application icon, which is located in the Disk 1 folder of the MCP folder on the *Kenwood TH-D7 In-Depth Manual* CD-ROM.
3. The Setup window appears briefly.
4. When the Welcome window appears, read its contents, then click on the **Next** button.
5. When the Software License Agreement window appears, read its contents, then click on the **Yes** button.
6. When the Choose Country Version window appears, select the TH-D7 model you have (TH-D7, TH-D7A, or TH-D7E) from the list, then click on the **Next** button.
7. When the Choose Destination Window appears, click on the **Next** button to install *MCP-D7* in its default location (*C:\Program Files\KENWOOD*) or click on the **Browse** button to install *MCP-D7* in a different location.
8. When the Select Program Folder window appears, you choose where the *MCP-D7* program will be installed. To install the MCP-D7 program icon in the KENWOOD program folder (the default selection), click on the **Next** button. To choose a different program folder, select it from the Existing Folders list, then click on the **Next** button. To install the icon in a new program folder, type its name in the Program Folders field, then click on the **Next** button.

9. Bar graphs appear to indicate the progress of the software installation.
10. When the Setup Complete window appears, click on the **Finish** button.
11. Press the **POWER** button to turn off the TH-D7.
12. Connect serial port COM 1 or COM 2 of the computer to the PC port of the TH-D7 using Kenwood's optional PG-4W cable or a compatible cable.

   That completes the installation of *MCP-D7*. Now you can configure the APRS software built into the TH-D7 using *MCP-D7* according to the following steps.
1. Press the **POWER** button to power the TH-D7.
2. If the TH-D7 displays [TNC___]PACKET, press the **TNC** button once.
3. From the **Start** menu, select **Programs**, then **Kenwood**, then **MCP-D7**.

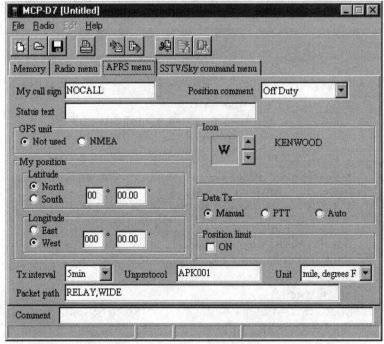

Figure 3-21—The APRS menu window displays the TH-D7 APRS software parameters that you may configure using MCP-D7.

4. As *MCP-D7* starts up, it briefly displays a Welcome window, then it displays its application window.
5. From the **Radio** menu, select the computer serial port (**COM1** or **COM2**) that is connected to the TH-D7 PC port.
6. Select the **APRS menu** tab.
7. When the APRS menu window appears, as illustrated in **Figure 3-21**, it displays 12 configurable TH-D7 APRS software parameters set at their default selection.
   a. If the TH-D7 was configured previously, you may load that configuration into the APRS menu window by clicking on the **Read** button or by selecting **Read** from the **Radio** menu.
   b. If you saved a previous configuration that you had set up using *MCP-D7*, you may load that configuration into the APRS menu window by clicking on the **Open** button or by selecting **Open** from the **File** menu.
8. Configure the APRS menu window parameters as required.
   a. My call sign—Enter your call sign. Remember to enter an SSID if one is desired. An SSID (for secondary station identifier) is a number (0-15) that follows a packet radio station call sign (and a hyphen). It is used to differentiate between two or more packet radio stations operating under the same call sign. For example, my APRS digipeater is WA1LOU-15 and my APRS mobile station is WA1LOU-8. Enter your call sign and SSID.
   b. Position comment—Select one of eight standard strings of text to be sent whenever the TH-D7 APRS software transmits your station's position packet. The selections are Off Duty, En Route, In Service, Returning, Committed, Special, Priority and Emergency. Selecting Special or Priority causes your station to be highlighted on the computer displays of other APRS stations that receive your packet. Selecting Emergency sets off alarms in the computers of other APRS stations that receive your packet, so this comment should only be selected if there actually is an emergency.
   c. Status text—Enter a short string of text to be sent whenever the TH-D7 APRS software transmits your station's position packet.
   d. GPS unit—Click on the **NMEA** button if there is an

NMEA-compatible GPS receiver connected to the TH-D7; if not, click on the **Not used** button.

e. My position—Enter the latitude and longitude of your station location. In the Latitude panel, click on the **N** or **S** button (for North or South latitude respectively), press **Tab**, then enter the latitude in degrees in the ° field. Press **Tab** again, then enter the latitude in minutes and hundredths of minutes in the ' field. In the Longitude panel, click on the **E** or **W** button (for East or West longitude respectively), press **Tab**, then enter the longitude in degrees in the ° field. Press **Tab** again, then enter the longitude in minutes and hundredths of minutes in the ' field. If any coordinate is less than 10, enter a 0 before the coordinate, for example, enter 05 for 5 minutes. If the longitude is less than 100°, enter one 0 before the longitude, and if the longitude is less than 10°, enter two 0s before the longitude, for example, enter 072 for 72° or 002 for 2°. If a GPS receiver is connected to the TH-D7, you may skip this step because the GPS receiver provides the coordinates automatically.

f. Icon—Click on the up and down arrows to select the icon you wish to represent your station on the APRS maps. This field allows you to choose one of the 15 icons that the TH-D7 can display. To choose an icon that the TH-D7 cannot display, click on the up and down arrows to select **Other**, then click on the down arrow in the Table field to select the icon table (/ or \) from which you will select the icon. Finally, click on the up and down arrows in the Symbol field to select the alphanumeric character that represents the icon you wish to use. Refer to Table 3-1 for the list of selectable symbols.

g. Data tx—Click the appropriate button (**Manual**, **PTT** or **Auto**) to determine how the TH-D7 APRS software sends position packets. If you select Manual, position packets are transmitted each time you press the BCON button on the TH-D7. If you select PTT, position packets are transmitted each time you release the PTT switch on the TH-D7. If you select Auto, position packets are transmitted according to the setting of the Tx interval parameter (from 30-second 5 to 30-minute intervals). Note that to enable the PTT and Auto selections, press the **BCON** button on the TH-D7 to cause the TH-D7 to display BCON.

h. Position limit—This parameter causes the TH-D7 to ignore packets received from stations beyond a selected distance (10 to 2500 miles/kilometers). To enable this option, click in the **ON** check box, press **Tab**, then type the desired distance in the Distance field (0010 to 2500 miles/kilometers in 10-mile/kilometer increments).

i. Tx interval—Click on the down arrow to select how often the TH-D7 APRS software transmits position packets (every 0.5, 1, 2, 3, 5, 10, 20, or 30 minutes).

j. Unprotocol—This parameter should be set to **APK001**.

k. Unit—Click on the down arrow to select how the TH-D7 will display distance and temperature (in miles and degrees Fahrenheit or kilometers and degrees Celsius respectively).

l. Packet path—Type the digipeater path you wish to use, for example, **VIA WA1LOU-15,WIDE**.

9. After you have selected all the desired parameters, click on the **Write** button or select **Write** from the **Radio** menu to transfer the configuration to the TH-D7. Click on the **Y** button (for Yes) when you are prompted "Do you want to write the data to the radio?" Note that this causes *MCP-D7* to transfer the parameters from its Memory, Radio and SSTV/Sky command menus, as well as its APRS menu.

10. To save this configuration, click on the **Save** button or select **Save** or **Save As...** from the File menu. When prompted, enter a file name for the configuration, then click on the **Save** button.

11. To quit *MCP-D7*, select **Exit** from the File menu.

12. On the TH-D7, select the lowest transmit power by pressing the **F** and **MENU** keys until the TH-D7 displays EL (for extremely low power; L indicates low power and H indicates high power).

13. If a GPS receiver is connected to the TH-D7, power it, then press the **POS** button. When the TH-D7 begins receiving position information from the GPS receiver, the display begins blinking, then it displays the grid square, latitude and longitude.

14. If you selected Auto or Manual in the Data tx option, press the **BCON** button to cause the TH-D7 to display BCON. If you selected PTT, depress and release the PTT switch momentarily.

   Step 14 causes the TH-D7 to transmit an APRS position

packet (the red LED on the top of the TH-D7 turns on during a transmission). If the TH-D7 receives your digipeated packet, the TH-D7 displays MY PACKET. This is a sure sign that you have configured the TH-D7 correctly. If the TH-D7 does not display MY PACKET, you may have to configure its Packet path parameter differently or increase its transmit power.

If the red LED did not turn on to indicate a transmission, check that the TH-D7's transmitter is not inhibited. Press the **MENU** button, then press **1, 5** and **5** again and check that TX INHIBIT is set to OFF. If it is set to ON, press the **OK** button, then press the **up** or **down** button to select **OFF**, then press the **OK** button again.

Configuring the TH-D7 TNC for APRS

The TH-D7 may be used for APRS by configuring its built-in TNC for APRS operation using any of the versions of APRS described above. To do so requires the following preliminary steps:
1. Press the **POWER** button to turn off the transceiver.
2. Connect the serial port of the computer running APRS to the PC port of the transceiver using Kenwood's optional PG-4W cable or a compatible cable.
3. Press the **POWER** button to power the transceiver.
4. Press the **TNC** button as may times as necessary (once or twice) until the transceiver displays [TNC___]PACKET.

Now, you may run the APRS software on your computer to configure the transceiver TNC.

WinAPRS Installation and Configuration

WinAPRS is a *Windows* (*95, 98,* or *NT*) version of APRS written by Keith Sproul, WU2Z, and Mark Sproul, KB2ICI.

The minimum computer requirements of *WinAPRS* are a PC with a 386 microprocessor running *Windows 95*. The recommended computer configuration is a PC with a 486 microprocessor and a 33-MHz clock with 8 Mbytes of RAM running *Windows 95, Windows NT,* or *Windows 3.1.* (Running under *Windows 3.1* requires the installation of the Win32S library, which is available at **http://www.ncsa.uiuc.edu/SDG/ Software/mosaic-w/faq/win32.html**.

WinAPRS is distributed as a compressed file, *waprs###.zip*, where *###* is the version number of the software, for example, *waprs228.zip*. Besides the *WinAPRS* application, this compressed file also contains documentation and a sufficient sampling of maps to get you up and running.

To decompress *WinAPRS*, use the shareware application *WinZip*, which is available from **http://www.winzip.com**.

The following procedures describe how to install and configure *WinAPRS*. These procedures assume that you are familiar with the operation of the *Windows*.

1. Power up your computer.
2. Double-click on the compressed *WinAPRS* files icon to start *WinZip*.
3. Select **Extract** from the **Actions** menu.
4. When the Extract window appears, click on the **All Files** and **Use Folder Names** buttons to enable them if they are not already enabled.
5. In the Folders/drives window, select the drive and folder where you wish *WinZip* to store the folder (called winaprs) which will contain the decompressed *WinAPRS* files.
6. Click on the **Extract** button and *WinZip* decompresses the *WinAPRS* files.
7. When decompression is completed, select **Exit** from the **File** menu.

That completes the installation of *WinAPRS*. Now you can configure *WinAPRS* according to the following steps. Remember that if you have not registered *WinAPRS*, you must configure the software each time you start it.

1. Assuming that your computer is already on, power up the rest of your APRS hardware (TNC, radio equipment and GPS receiver, if any).
2. Tune the radio to the local APRS operating frequency (144.39, 445.925 and 10.1515 MHz are the national APRS operating frequencies) and APRS mode (FM on VHF and UHF, LSB on HF).
3. Double-click on the **winaprs** application icon to start *WinAPRS*.
4. When the *WinAPRS* start-up window appears, click on the **OK** button.
5. When the TNC Selection window appears, as illustrated in

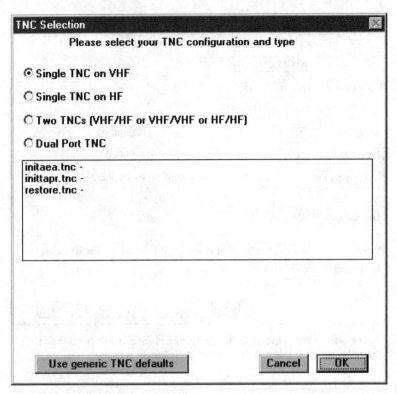

Figure 3-22—The TNC Selection window allows you to enter your basic TNC setup into WinAPRS.

Figure 3-22, click on the button that represents your TNC configuration (one TNC on VHF or HF, two TNCs, or a dual-port TNC), then click on the **OK** button.

6. When the *WinAPRS* main window appears, select **Station** from the **Settings** menu.

7. When the Station Settings window appears, as illustrated in **Figure 3-23**, configure its parameter as required.

   a. Callsign—Type your call sign, then press **Tab**. Remember to enter an SSID if one is desired. An SSID (for secondary station identifier) is a number (0-15) that follows a packet radio station call sign (and a hyphen). It is used to differentiate between two or more packet radio stations operating under the same call sign. For example, my APRS digipeater is WA1LOU-15 and my APRS mobile station is WA1LOU-8.

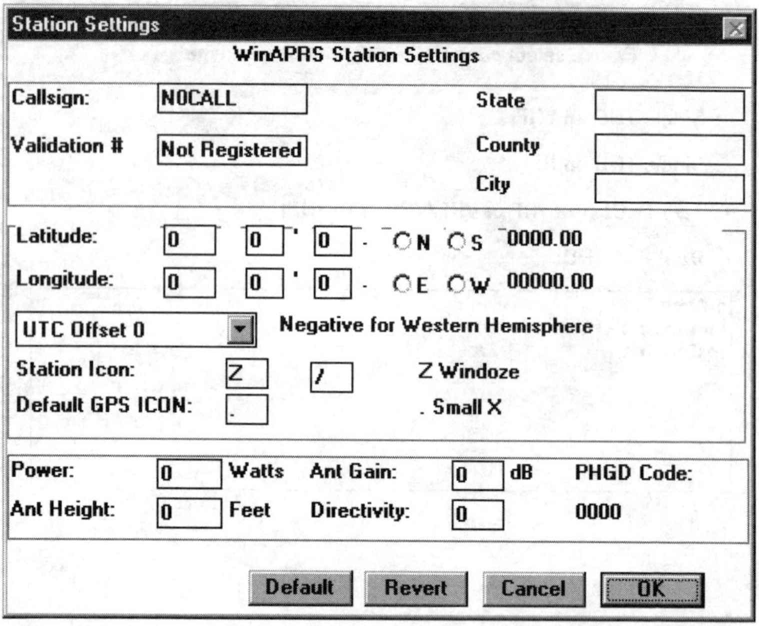

Figure 3-23—You enter the majority of the information concerning your station in the WinAPRS Station Settings window.

Enter your call sign and SSID.

b. Validation #—Type your registration number, then press **Tab**. (Avoiding reconfiguration each time you start *WinAPRS* should be plenty of incentive to register the software.)

c. State—Type the two-letter abbreviation for the state or province where your APRS station is located, then press **Tab**.

d. County—Type the name of the county where your APRS station is located, then press **Tab**.

e. City—Type the name of the town or city where your APRS station is located, then press **Tab**.

f. Latitude—Type the latitude (in degrees, minutes and seconds) where your APRS station is located. Press the **Tab** key after each entry.

g. N / S—Click on the appropriate button **N** or **S** for North or South latitude respectively, then press **Tab**.

h. Longitude—Type the longitude (in degrees, minutes and seconds) where your APRS station is located. Press the **Tab** key after each entry.

i. E / W—Click on the appropriate button **E** or **W** for East or West longitude respectively, then press **Tab**.

j. UTC Offset—From this menu, select the number of hours (+ or –) your local time differs from Greenwich Mean/ Universal Time, then press **Tab**.

k. Station Icon—Type the alphanumeric character that stands for the icon you wish to represent your station on the APRS maps (for example, p for puppy), then press **Tab**. Refer to Table 3-1 for the list of selectable symbols.

l. Default GPS ICON—Leave this parameter at its default setting by pressing **Tab**.

m. Power—Type your transmitter power in watts, then press **Tab**. The maximum meaningful entry in this field is 81 watts. If you enter anything larger than 81, *WinAPRS* still calculates your station's coverage area as if its transmitter power was 81 watts. The purpose of this limitation is to promote the use of minimum power in APRS networks.

n. Ant Height—Type your station's Height Above Average Terrain (HAAT) in feet, then press **Tab**.

o. Ant Gain—Type the station antenna's gain in dB, then press **Enter**.

p. Directivity—Type the direction (in degrees) that station antenna favors. For North, type 360 degrees and for an omnidirectional antenna, type 0 degrees. If local terrain affects the operation of your omnidirectional antenna, however, you may type a figure that represents the direction that your antenna favors. For example, if a mountain to your west causes your omnidirectional antenna to favor the east, type **90**.

q. When you are finished configuring the parameters in the Station Settings window, click on the **OK** button.

8. The icon you selected in step 7k now appears on the map at the longitude and latitude you entered.

9. Select **APRS** from the **Settings** menu.

10. When the *WinAPRS* Settings window appears, as illustrated

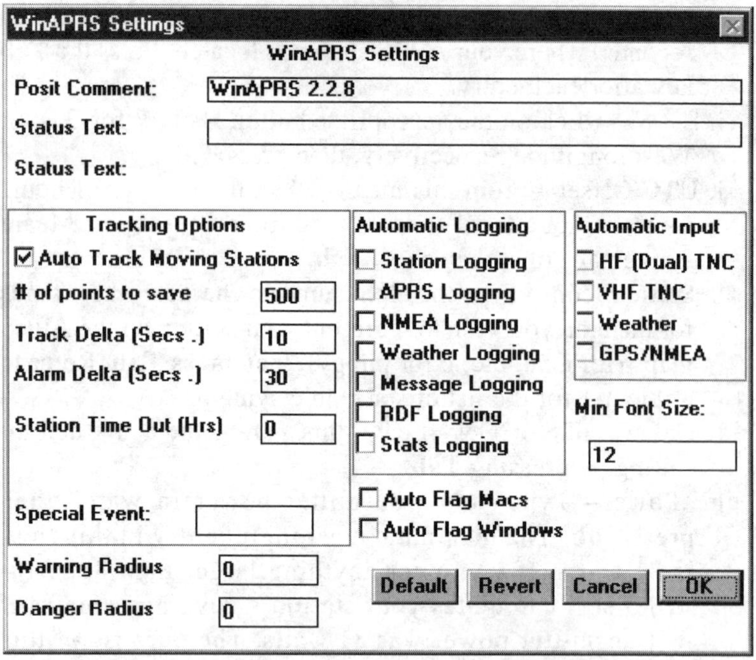

Figure 3-24—When the WinAPRS Settings window appears, enter your station's status text.

in **Figure 3-24**, configure the following parameters as required.

a. In the Status Text field, you may type a remark that the program appends to each APRS position packet that it transmits. The remark can be related to your name, location, or whatever you feel is appropriate. If you don't know what you want as a comment at this time, you can access the *WinAPRS* Settings window later to add a comment after you see what other stations on the air are using.

b. In the Automatic Input panel, select either **VHF TNC** or **HF (Dual) TNC**, depending on your TNC configuration. If a GPS receiver is connected to your TNC or computer, also select **GPS/NMEA**.

11. Click on the **OK** button to close the *WinAPRS* Settings window.

12. Select **Serial port** from the **Settings** menu.

13. When the Serial Port Settings window appears, as illustrated in **Figure 3-25**, determine which panel in the window applies to your TNC configuration (VHF or HF/Dual).

14. Select the following parameters in that panel to conform with the parameters used for communications between your TNC and the computer serial (COM) port that is connected to your TNC.

    a. Number—Type the number of the computer serial (COM) port that is connected to your TNC.

    b. Speed—Type the data rate used for communications between your TNC and computer.

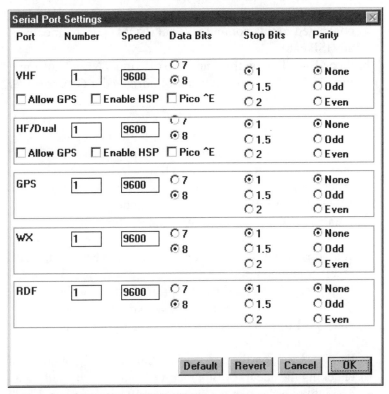

Figure 3-25—The Serial Port Settings window allows you to set communications parameters for the computer's connections to the TNC and GPS receiver.

c. Data Bits—Click on the appropriate button for the number of bits (7 or 8) that represent an alphanumeric or control character used in communications between your TNC and computer.

d. Stop Bits—Click on the appropriate button for the number of bits (1, 1.5 or 2) that follow a character (to indicate its end) used in communications between your TNC and computer.

e. Parity—Click on the appropriate button for the method of checking the accuracy of a received character by adding an extra bit in order that the character will have an even or odd number of one bits depending on the type of parity used (even, odd, or none).

f. Allow GPS—Click on this check box if a GPS receiver is connected to another computer serial (COM) port.

g. Enable HSP—Click on this check box if a GPS receiver is connected to this computer serial (COM) port by means of an HSP cable.

h. Pico ^E—Click on this check box if your TNC a PacComm PicoPacket TNC with two serial ports and a GPS receiver is connected to one of them.

15. If a GPS receiver is connected to a computer serial (COM) port, select the following parameters in the GPS panel.

a. Number—Type the number of the computer serial (COM) port that is connected to your GPS receiver.

b. Speed—Type the data rate used for communications between your GPS receiver and computer.

c. Data Bits—Click on the appropriate button for the number of bits (7 or 8) that represent an alphanumeric or control character used in communications between your GPS receiver and computer.

d. Stop Bits—Click on the appropriate button for the number of bits (1, 1.5 or 2) that follow a character (to indicate its end) used in communications between your GPS receiver and computer.

e. Parity—Click on the appropriate button for the method of checking the accuracy of a received character by adding an extra bit in order that the character will have an even or odd number of one bits depending on the type of parity used (even, odd or none).

16. When you are finished configuring the parameters in the Serial Port Settings window, click on the **OK** button.
17. Select **TNC** from the **Settings** menu.
18. When the *WinAPRS* TNC Settings window appears, as illustrated in **Figure 3-26**, configure the following parameters as required.

a. In the Unproto APRSW Via field, type the digipeater path you wish to use, for example, VIA WA1LOU-15,.

b. On the left side of the window, select your TNC Type

Receive Only—Click on this button if your configuration is for receiving APRS only.

Single Port—Click on this button if your TNC has one radio port (HF or VHF).

Dual Port—Click on this button if your TNC has separate HF and VHF radio ports.

Two Ports—Click on this button if your TNC has two VHF radio ports.

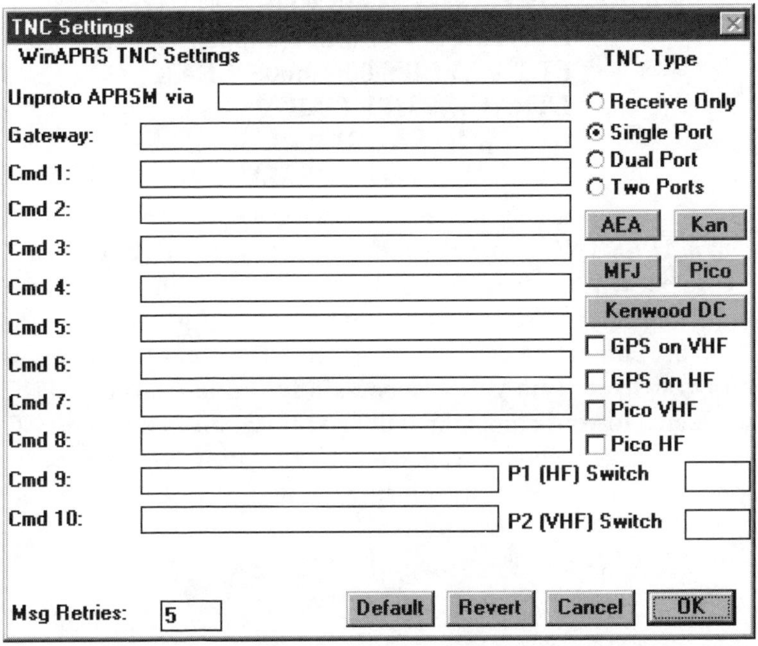

Figure 3-26—To fine-tune WinAPRS for compatibility with your TNC brand, model and configuration, use the TNC Settings window.

c. Click on the appropriate button for your brand of TNC: **AEA**, **Kan** (for Kantronics), **MFJ**, **Pico** (for PacComm PicoPacket), or **Kenwood DC** (for the Kenwood TH-D7 transceiver). (After clicking on a button, the appropriate commands for that TNC are loaded into the command fields of the *WinAPRS* TNC Settings window.)

d. If a GPS receiver is connected to the computer serial (COM) port by means of an HSP cable, click on **GPS on VHF** if the GPS receiver is connected to the VHF port or **GPS on HF** if the GPS receiver is connected to the HF port.

e. If your TNC is a PacComm PicoPacket with two serial ports and a GPS receiver is connected to one of the ports, click **Pico VHF** if the GPS receiver is connected to the VHF port or **Pico HF** if the GPS receiver is connected to the HF port.

f. If your TNC is a KPC-3+ with version 3.8 (or later) firmware and a GPS receiver is connected to the radio port of the TNC, then enter the following commands in any empty Cmd fields:

> **GPSHEAD 1 $GPRMC**
> **LTP 1 GPS VIA (your digipeater path)**
> **BLT 1 EVERY 00:10:00 CLEAR**
> **LTRACK 5 LT1 TIME**
> **GPSTIME VALID RMC**
> **GPSPORT 4800 NORMAL CHECKSUM**

19. When you are finished configuring the parameters in the *WinAPRS* TNC Settings window, click on the **OK** button.

20. Select **Open VHF TNC** or **Open HF TNC (dual)** from the Settings menu depending on your TNC configuration.

This completes the installation and basic configuration of WinAPRS. If WinAPRS successfully initialized the TNC connected to your computer and the radio connected to the TNC is tuned to an active APRS channel, stations should begin appearing on the WinAPRS map window.

Table 3-1
APRS Station Icons and Symbols

Table	Symbol	GPSxyz	Description
/	!	BB	Police, Sheriff
/	"	BC	reserved
/	#	BD	Digipeater (Green Hollow Star)
/	$	BE	Phone
/	%	BF	DX Cluster
/	&	BG	Gateway
/		BH	Aircraft (Small)
/	(	BI	Cloudy
/	)	BJ	
/	*	BK	Snowmobile
/	+	BL	Red Cross
/	,	BM	Boy Scouts
/	-	BN	House, QTH with Vertical Antenna
/	.	BO	X (Small)
/	/	BP	Dot
/	0	P0	Circle (Numbered)
/	1	P1	Circle (Numbered)
/	2	P2	Circle (Numbered)
/	3	P3	Circle (Numbered)
/	4	P4	Circle (Numbered)
/	5	P5	Circle (Numbered)
/	6	P6	Circle (Numbered)
/	7	P7	Circle (Numbered)
/	8	P8	Circle (Numbered)
/	9	P9	Circle (Numbered)
/	:	MR	Fire
/	;	MS	Campground, Tent, Portable
/	<	MT	Motorcycle
/	=	MU	Railroad Engine
/	>	MV	Car
/	?	MW	File Server, Position Server
/	@	MX	Hurricane, Tropical Storm)
/	A	PA	Aid Station
/	B	PB	BBS
/	C	PC	Canoe
/	D	PD	
/	E	PE	Eyeball
/	F	PF	
/	G	PG	Grid Square (6-digit)
/	H	PH	Hotel (Blue Dot)
/	I	PI	TCP/IP
/	J	PJ	
/	K	PK	School
/	L	PL	
/	M	PM	MacAPRS
/	N	PN	NTS Station

Table	Symbol	GPSxyz	Description
/	O	PO	Balloon
/	P	PP	Police Car
/	Q	PQ	
/	R	PR	Recreation Vehicle
/	S	PS	Space Shuttle
/	T	PT	SSTV
/	U	PU	Bus
/	V	PV	ATV
/	W	PW	National Weather Service Site
/	X	PX	Helicopter
/	Y	PY	Yacht, Sailboat
/	Z	PZ	WinAPRS
/	[	HS	Runner, Jogger
/	\	HT	Triangle (Direction Finding)
/	]	HU	PBBS, Mailbox
/	^	HV	Aircraft (Large)
/	_	HW	Weather Station
/	`	HX	Satellite Ground Station
/	a	LA	Ambulance
/	b	LB	Bicycle
/	c	LC	
/	d	LD	Fire Department
/	e	LE	Horse
/	f	LF	Fire Truck
/	g	LG	Glider, Hang Glider
/	h	LH	Hospital
/	i	LI	Islands on the Air (IOTA)
/	j	LJ	Jeep
/	k	LK	Truck
/	l	LL	
/	m	LM	MIC-Encoder Repeater
/	n	LN	Node
/	o	LO	Emergency Operations Center (EOC)
/	p	LP	Rover, Dog, Puppy
/	q	LQ	Grid Square (4-digit)
/	r	LR	Antenna
/	s	LS	Power Boat
/	t	LT	Truck Stop
/	u	LU	Truck (18-Wheeler)
/	v	LV	Van
/	w	LW	Water Station
/	x	LX	Xaprs (UNIX APRS)
/	y	LY	House, QTH with Yagi Antenna
/	z	LZ	
/	{	J1	
/	|	J2	reserved
/	}	J3	
	~	J3	reserved

Table	Symbol	GPSxyz	Description
\	!	OB	Emergency
\	"	OC	reserved
\	#	OD	Digipeater (Green Numbered Star)
\	$	OE	Bank or ATM
\	%	OF	
\	&	OG	Gateway (Numbered Diamond)
\		OH	Crash Site
\	(	OI	Cloudy
\	)	OJ	
\	*	OK	Snow
\	+	OL	Church
\	,	OM	Girl Scouts
\	-	ON	House
\	.	OO	Vicinity Ambiguous Plot
\	/	OP	
\	0	A0	Circle (Numbered)
\	1	A1	
\	2	A2	
\	3	A3	
\	4	A4	
\	5	A5	
\	6	A6	
\	7	A7	
\	8	A8	
\	9	A9	Gas Station
\	:	NR	Driving Hail
\	;	NS	Park, Picnic Area
\	<	NT	Advisory
\	=	NU	
\	>	NV	Car (Numbered)
\	?	NW	Information Kiosk
\	@	NX	Hurricame, Tropical Storm
\	A	AA	Box (Numbered)
\	B	AB	Blowing Snow
\	C	AC	Coast Guard
\	D	AD	Drizzle
\	E	AE	Smoke
\	F	AF	Freezing Rain
\	G	AG	Snow Shower
\	H	AH	Haze
\	I	AI	Rain Shower
\	J	AJ	Lightning
\	K	AK	Kenwood Radio
\	L	AL	Lighthouse
\	M	AM	
\	N	AN	Navigation Buoy
\	O	AO	

(continued)

Table	Symbol	GPSxyz	Description
\	P	AP	Parking
\	Q	AQ	Earthquake
\	R	AR	Restaurant
\	S	AS	Satellite, Pacsat
\	T	AT	Thunderstorm
\	U	AU	Sunny
\	V	AV	VORTAC Navigational Aid
\	W	AW	National Weather Service Site (Numbered)
\	X	AX	Pharmacy
\	Y	AY	
\	Z	AZ	
\	[	DS	Wall Cloud
\	/	DT	
\	]	DU	
\	^	DV	Aircraft (Numbered)
\	_	DW	Weather Site (Numbered)
\	`	DX	Rain
\	a	SA	ARRL, ARES
\	b	SB	Duststorm, Sandstorm
\	c	SC	Civil Defense (RACES) (Numbered)
\	d	SD	DX Spot by Call Sign
\	e	SE	Sleet
\	f	SF	Funnel Cloud
\	g	SG	Gale Flags
\	h	SH	Ham Radio Store
\	i	SI	
\	j	SJ	Work Zone
\	k	SK	
\	l	SL	Area Locations (Box, Circle, etc.)
\	m	SM	Value Signpost, Milepost (3-digit)
\	n	SN	Triangle (Numbered)
\	o	SO	Small Circle
\	p	SP	Partly Cloudy
\	q	SQ	
\	r	SR	Restrooms
\	s	SS	Ship, Boat (Numbered)
\	t	ST	Tornado
\	u	SU	Truck (Numbered)
\	v	SV	Van (Numbered)
\	w	SW	Flooding
\	x	SX	
\	y	SY	
\	z	SZ	
\	{	Q1	Fog
\			Q2	
\	}	Q3	
\	~	Q4	

4

OPERATION

T his chapter describes how to use the APRS software you installed and configured in the previous chapter. After a brief description of APRS on-the-air operating parameters, the chapter describes the most common APRS operating functions and how to perform each function with each version of APRS.

OPERATING PARAMETERS

On VHF, most APRS activity in North America occurs on 2 meters at 144.39 MHz. You may also find some local pockets of activity on 145.79 MHz, but that activity is likely to QSY to 144.39 shortly. A data rate of 1200 bit/s is the norm on both channels.

On UHF, 445.925 MHz is the focus of UHF APRS activity using 9600 or 1200 bit/s.

On HF, 10.151.51 MHz LSB is the frequency of choice and 300 bit/s is the data rate. Note that the carrier is actually 2125 kHz down from 10.151.51 MHz, so it *is* within the Amateur Radio allocated frequencies.

OPERATING FUNCTIONS

The rest of this chapter is devoted to describing the most common operating functions of APRS, that is, those functions that you are likely to use regularly. The description of each function is followed by the steps for performing that function with each version of APRS that supports it. Note that all versions of APRS do *not* support all APRS functions.

Navigating the Software

You must be able to navigate APRS maps in order to become an expert APRS operator. This section describes how to get around in each version of APRS.

Map Display Basics

There are different basic map display procedures for each version of APRS that uses maps.

APRS (DOS)

With *APRS (DOS)*, pressing the Space Bar to display and refresh (redraw) a map.

APRS+SA

In *APRS+SA*, to display APRS data on a DeLorme *Street Atlas* map:

1. Start *Street Atlas*.
2. Click on the Maps tab.
3. When the Maps tab appears, click on the desired button in the column of buttons on the left side of the window to display the desired APRS data on the *Street Atlas* map. For example, to display all the APRS data received on the map, click on the **1 All Reports** button.
4. After clicking the desired button, the *Street Atlas* map appears displaying the received APRS data.

MacAPRS

With *MacAPRS*, you refresh and display a map by entering **Command-L** or selecting Clear/Redraw from the Display menu.

You can center the map on the current position of the cursor by pressing the **Home** key in *APRS (DOS)* or by selecting Center View from the Display menu of *MacAPRS*.

pocketAPRS

In *pocketAPRS*, to display a map:

1. Tap the MENU icon on the Palm III.
2. Select Map from the Views menu.

To move a *pocketAPRS* map in the map window, drag the map with the stylus.

WinAPRS

In *WinAPRS*, select Auto Refresh Maps from Display menu to cause the program to refresh the maps every three minutes without user intervention.

Magnifying Maps

All versions of APRS that use maps permit you to zoom in (magnify) and zoom out of the maps.

APRS (DOS)

You magnify a map by pressing the **Page Down** key in *APRS (DOS)*. You may zoom out of a map by pressing the **Page Up** key.

APRS+SA

In *APRS+SA*, pressing the **Page Down** and **Page Up** keys zoom in and out of the *Street Atlas* maps, respectively.

MacAPRS

Pressing the **Page Down** and **Page Up** keys in *MacAPRS* zooms in and out of the APRS maps. You may also select **Zoom In 2x (Page Down)** or **Zoom In 4x** from the Display menu in order to magnify the map two or four times, respectively, and you may select **Zoom Out 2x (Page Up)** from the Display menu.

You may return to the original magnification of the map by pressing the **Home** key in *MacAPRS*. Entering **Command-H** or selecting **Home View (Home)** from the Display menu in *MacAPRS* also performs the same function.

You may zoom in any portion of a map that you desire in *MacAPRS* by pressing the **Option** key, while clicking on the mouse button and drawing a rectangle of the portion of the map you wish to magnify.

pocketAPRS

You magnify a map in *pocketAPRS* by selecting the plus (+) magnifying glass icon at the bottom of the map window, then tapping the location on the map you wish to magnify. You zoom out of a map by selecting the minus (–) magnifying glass icon at the bottom of the map window, then tapping the map. You can also zoom in and out of a map by selecting the level of magnification you desire from the pick list at the top of the map window.

You may return to the original magnification of the map in *pocketAPRS* by tapping the X magnifying glass icon at the bottom of the map window.

WinAPRS

Pressing the **Page Down** and **Page Up** keys in *WinAPRS* zooms in and out of the APRS maps.

You may zoom in any portion of a map in *WinAPRS* by clicking on the Right mouse button and drawing a rectangle of the portion of the map you wish to magnify. Then press the **Page Down** key.

You may return to the original magnification of the map in *WinAPRS* by pressing Home, pressing **H**, or selecting Home View from the Display menu.

Tracking

The ability to track moving objects on a map is the primary function (and attraction) of APRS. This function has made APRS an appealing tool for public service communications. The dynamics of tracking public service events require the tracking power of APRS and the ability to replay the track of a moving object just adds to this power.

Tracking requires the moving object to transmit its position as it traverses its route. This may be accomplished automatically via a GPS unit configured to the transmitter in the moving object or manually via operator control. Manual operator control may be performed by an operator inputting position information into a computer running APRS aboard the moving object or remotely by an operator, who placed a moving object like a hurricane on an APRS map. In either case, each time a new position is transmitted for a moving object, the icon of that object appears in a new position on the APRS map. (**Figure 4-1** illustrates the track of K1TRS-12 along I-84 in central Connecticut. The eight appearances of the icon on the map indicates the transmission of eight new positions by the APRS equipment aboard K1TRS-12.)

Replaying the track of a moving object is performed differently with the various versions of APRS. For starters, to replay the track of one object in *APRS+SA*, you must select the object beforehand.

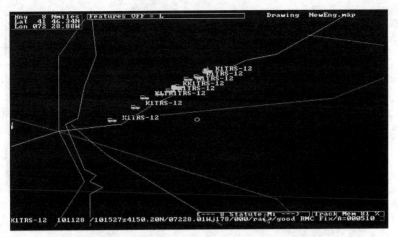

Figure 4-1—APRS (DOS) tracks K1TRS-12 along I-84 in central Connecticut.

With *MacAPRS* and *WinAPRS*, you can select one moving object at any time to replay the entire track of that object only.

Another difference is how the various versions of APRS display a replay of a track. With *APRS (DOS)*, a replay of a tracked object duplicates the original display of that object, that is, the icon of the moving object is displayed at each position along its route wherever it transmitted a new position. (With *APRS (DOS)*, a replay of the track illustrated in Figure 4-1 would appear exactly like Figure 4-1.) With *APRS+SA*, *MacAPRS* and *WinAPRS*, the software draws a solid line along the route of the tracked object from the beginning to the end of its route. (**Figure 4-2** illustrates the original track of K1TRS-12 with *MacAPRS* and **Figure 4-3** illustrates the replay of that same track with *MacAPRS*. *WinAPRS* performs in a similar fashion.)

The following describes how to track and replay tracked stations with each version of APRS.

APRS (DOS)

To replay the track of a station or station(s) in memory:

1. Press **O** (for Operations).
2. Press **R** (for Replay).
3. Press **Enter** to replay all the stations or type a call sign to replay a single station.

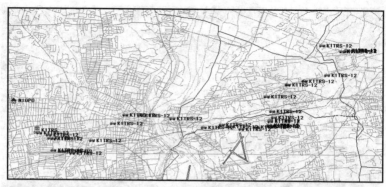

Figure 4-2—MacAPRS tracks K1TRS-12 along I-84 in central Connecticut.

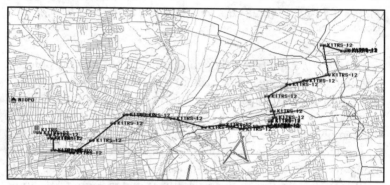

Figure 4-3—MacAPRS replays the track of K1TRS-12 along I-84 in central Connecticut.

4. Press **F** or **S** to replay the track faster or slower, respectively.

To replay a track stored in a track history file:

1. Press **F** (for File).
2. Press **R** (for Replay).
3. Type the name of the track history file you wish to replay.
4. Press **Enter** to replay all the stations or type a call sign to replay a single station.
5. Press **F** or **S** to replay the track faster or slower, respectively.

APRS+SA

To track a station with *APRS+SA*:

1. Click on the Track tab.

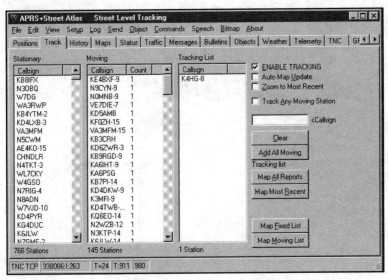

Figure 4-4—The APRS+SA *Track tab after selecting K4HG-8 for tracking.*

2. When the Track tab appears, click on the Enable Tracking box if it does not contain a check mark.

3. Double-click on the call sign of the station you wish to track from the Moving or Stationary list or type the call sign in the <Callsign field and press **Enter**. After double-clicking or pressing *Enter*, the call sign of the selected station will appear in the Tracking List. (Unless you know that a stationary station is going to go mobile, there is no point selecting a station to track from the Stationary list.) (**Figure 4-4** shows the Track tab after selecting K4HG-8 for tracking.)

4. Click on the Map All Reports or **Map Most Recent** button to view the track of the selected station on the *Street Atlas* map. Clicking Map All Reports results in a track that represents all the position reports received from the selected station from the time you began tracking that station. Clicking Map Most Recent results in a track that represents only the most recent position reports received from the selected station. (**Figures 4-5** and **4-6** contrast the results of the Map All Reports and Map Most Recent

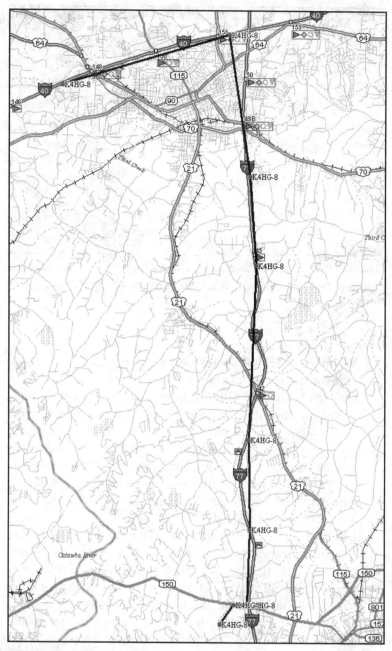

Figure 4-5—The APRS+SA *Map All Reports function displays all the position reports of the tracked station (K4HG-8).*

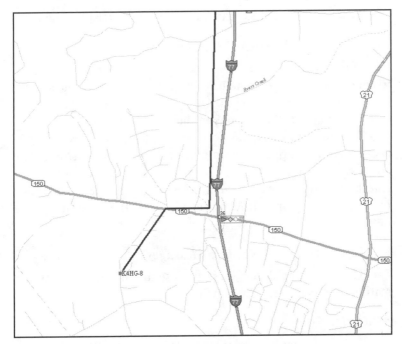

Figure 4-6—The **APRS+SA** *Map Most Recent function only displays recent position reports of the tracked station (K4HG-8).*

functions with regards to the track of K4HG-8.)

MacAPRS

To replay the track of a station with *MacAPRS*:
1. Choose the station whose track you wish to replay.
2. Click on the most recent icon (the last position received) of that station on the map.
3. Select Replay Selected Station from the Display menu or type **Command-R**.

WinAPRS

To replay the track of a station with *WinAPRS*:
1. Choose the station whose track you wish to replay.
2. Click on the most recent icon (the last position received) of that station on the map.

3. Press **R** or select **Replay Track** from the Display menu.

Keyboard Communications

Sometimes an APRS map itself is not enough and you have to contact another station to pass information concerning activity being displayed on the map. Or you may have a need to pass information to all the stations in the APRS network.

The authors of APRS foresaw this need and as a result, the software supports communications in real-time. The software accomplishes this by permitting you to send one-line messages to any active station in the APRS network or by sending multiple-line bulletins to all the stations in the network.

Sending Messages

The following describes how to send a message to another station with each version of APRS.

APRS (DOS)

To send a message to another station with *APRS (DOS)*:
1. Press **S** (for Send).
2. At the To: prompt, type the call sign of the station that is the intended recipient of the message.
3. At the Entr MsgText: prompt, type the contents of the message.

APRS+SA

To send a message to another station with *APRS+SA*:
1. Select Send Message from the Send menu or type **Ctrl-P**.
2. When the Message window appears, type the call sign of the intended recipient of the message in the Callsign To: field.
3. Press **TAB**, then enter the text of the message in the Message Text field.
4. Click on the **Send** button.

MacAPRS

To send a message to another station with *MacAPRS*:
1. Select New Message... from the Lists menu or type **Command-M**.
2. In the To: field, type the call sign of the station that is the

intended recipient of the message.

3. Press **TAB**, then enter the contents of the message in the Msg: field.

4. Click on the **OK** button.

pocketAPRS

To send a message to another station with *pocketAPRS*:

1. Tap the **MENU** icon on the Palm III

2. Select Send Message from the Main menu.

3. In the To: field, type the call sign of the station that is the intended recipient of the message.

4. Type the contents of the message in the field below the To: field.

5. Click on the **Send** button.

TH-D7

To send a message to another station with the TH-D7:

1. Press the **MSG** button.

2. Press the **up** or **down** button so that the cursor appears next to INPUT, then press the **OK** button.

3. At the TO: prompt, type the call sign and SSID of the intended recipient of your message using the TH-D7 front panel buttons.

4. Press the **OK** button (once or twice) to cause the cursor appears at the beginning of the bottom line of the TH-D7 display.

5. Type your message using the TH-D7 front panel buttons.

6. Press the **OK** button twice. This causes the TH-D7 to transmit your message.

WinAPRS

To send a message to another station with *WinAPRS*:

1. Press **F7** or select **New Message** from the Lists menu.

2. When the New Message Dialog box appears, type call sign of the station that is the intended recipient of the message in the To: field.

3. Type the contents of the message in the Msg: field.

4. Click on the **OK** button.

Reading Messages

The following describes how to read a message from another station with each version of APRS.

APRS (DOS)

To read a message from another station with *APRS (DOS)*, press **R** (for Read) and a window appears that lists the message sent by your station and addressed to your station. (**Figure 4-7** illustrates the message window.)

APRS+SA

To read messages from other stations with *APRS+SA*, click on the Traffic tab to view a list of all the messages sent and received by your station.

MacAPRS

To read a message from another station with *MacAPRS*, select Message List from the Lists menu or type **Command-4** and the Message List window appears containing all the messages sent and received by your station. Note that when your station receives a message that was specifically addressed to it, the Message List window appears automatically.

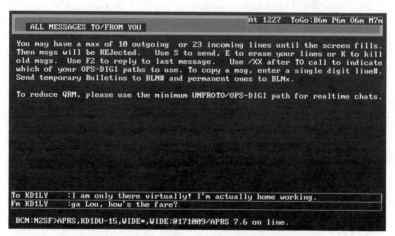

Figure 4-7—The message window in **APRS (DOS)** *lists messages sent by your station and addressed to your station.*

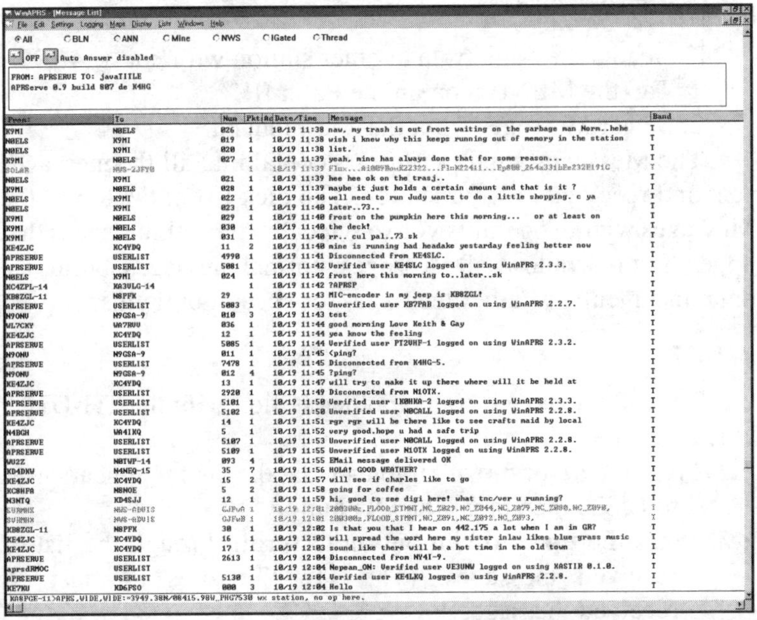

Figure 4-8—The Message List window in WinAPRS *lists all the messages sent and received by your station.*

The messages are color-coded to differentiate messages addressed to (red) or from you (blue) from those addressed to other stations (black). Color-coding also differentiates messages sent by your station that have and have not been received by their intended recipient (green for acknowledged messages, blue for unacknowledged messages). (**Figure 4-8** illustrates the *WinAPRS* Message List window, which is very similar to the *MacAPRS* Message List window.)

By default, the *MacAPRS* Message List displays all the messages and bulletins sent and received by your station. By clicking one of the buttons at the top of the Message List window, the window will only display bulletins (**BLN** button), announcements (**ANN** button), messages sent by your station and addressed to your station (**Mine** button), National Weather Service announcements (**NWS** button), messages relayed via an Internet gateway (**IGated** button), and threaded messages (**Thread** button). Clicking the **All** button causes the Message List to return to its default, that is, displaying all messages and bulletins.

pocketAPRS

To read a message from another station with *pocketAPRS:*
1. Tap the MENU icon on the Palm III.
2. Select Messages from the Views menu.

The Messages window appears containing all the messages sent and received by your station. The pick list at the top of the Messages window permits you to select the type of messages that appear in the window: all messages, normal messages, bulletins, announcements, weather messages, or special bulletins.

TH-D7

To read a message from another station with the TH-D7:
1. Press the **MSG** button.
2. Press the **up** or **down** button so that the cursor appears next to LIST, then press the **OK** button.
3. Press the **up** or **down** button to scroll through the list of received messages. (The TH-D7 stores the last 16 received messages.)
4. When you have located the message you wish to read, press the **OK** button when you are ready to read the second half of the message. (The TH-D7 initially displays the first 24 characters of a message. Pressing **OK** reveals the second 24 characters of a message.
5. When you are finished reading the message, press the **ESC** button twice.

WinAPRS

To read a message from another station with *WinAPRS*, select Message List from the Lists menu and the Message List window appears containing all the messages sent and received by your station.

The messages are color-coded to differentiate messages addressed to (red) or from you (blue) from those addressed to other stations (black). Color-coding also differentiates messages sent by your station that have and have not been received by their intended recipient (green for acknowledged messages, blue for unacknowledged messages). (Figure 4-8 illustrates the *WinAPRS* Message List window.)

By default, the *WinAPRS* Message List displays all the

messages and bulletins sent and received by your station. By clicking one of the buttons at the top of the Message List window, the window will only display bulletins (**BLN** button), announcements (**ANN** button), messages sent by your station and addressed to your station (**Mine** button), National Weather Service announcements (**NWS** button), messages relayed via an Internet gateway (**IGated** button), and threaded messages (**Thread** button). Clicking the **All** button causes the Message List to return to its default, that is, displaying all messages and bulletins.

Sending Bulletins

The following describes how to send a bulletin to other stations with each version of APRS.

APRS (DOS)

To send a bulletin to other stations with *APRS (DOS)*:
1. Press **S** (for Send).
2. At the To: prompt, type **BLN1**.
3. At the Entr MsgText: prompt, type the contents of one line of the bulletin.
4. If your bulletin is one line in length, then you are finished. If your bulletin is longer, press **S** again.
5. The To: prompt defaults to BLN2. Press **Enter**.
6. At the Entr MsgText: prompt, type the contents of the second line of the bulletin.
7. Stop if you are finished entering the bulletin or continue pressing **S** until you finish entering each line of a multiple line bulletin (up to a maximum of 9 lines, BLN1 to BLN9).

APRS+SA

To send a bulletin to other stations with *APRS+SA*:
1. Select **Send Bulletin** from the Send menu or type **Ctrl-B**.
2. When the Bulletin window appears, enter the contents of the bulletin in the Bulletins field.
3. Click on the **Send** button.

MacAPRS

To send a bulletin to other stations with *MacAPRS*:

1. Select New Message... from the Lists menu or type **Command-M**.
2. Click on the **Bulletin** button.
3. Press **TAB**, then enter the contents of the bulletin in the Msg: field.
4. Click on the **OK** button.

pocketAPRS

To send a bulletin to other stations with *pocketAPRS*:
1. Tap the MENU icon on the Palm III
2. Select Send Message from the Main menu.
3. Select Bulletin from the pick list to the right of the To: field.
4. Type the contents of the bulletin in the field below the To: field.
5. Click on the **Send** button.

TH-D7

To send a bulletin to other stations with the TH-D7:
1. Press the **MSG** button.
2. Press the **up** or **down** button so that the cursor appears next to INPUT, then press the **OK** button.
3. At the TO: prompt, type **BLN0** or **BLNA** (for the first message line of the bulletin) using the TH-D7 front panel buttons.
4. Press the **OK** button (once or twice) to cause the cursor appears at the beginning of the bottom line of the TH-D7 display.
5. Type the bulletin using the TH-D7 front panel buttons.
6. Press the **OK** button twice. This causes the TH-D7 to transmit the bulletin.
7. To transmit additional message lines, repeat steps 1 through 6, however, in step 3, make sure to increase the number or letter following BLN by one in order to indicate the proper sequence of message lines comprising the bulletin. For example, if the bulletin contained three message lines, you would type **BLN0** at the TO: prompt for the first line, **BLN1** for the second line, and **BLN3** for the third line.

WinAPRS

To send a bulletin to other stations with *WinAPRS*:
1. Press **F7** or select **New Message** from the Lists menu.

2. When the New Message Dialog box appears, click on the **Bulletin** button.

3. Type the contents of the bulletin in the Msg: field.

4. Click on the **OK** button.

Reading Bulletins

The following describes how to read bulletins with each version of APRS.

APRS (DOS)

To read bulletins with *APRS (DOS)*, press **B** (for Bulletins) and a window appears that lists the bulletins received to your station. (**Figure 4-9** illustrates the bulletin window.)

APRS+SA

To read bulletins from other stations with *APRS+SA*, click on the Bulletins tab to view a list of all the bulletins sent and received by your station.

MacAPRS

To read bulletins with *MacAPRS*, select Message List from the Lists menu or type **Command-4** and the Message List window appears containing all the bulletins sent and received by your

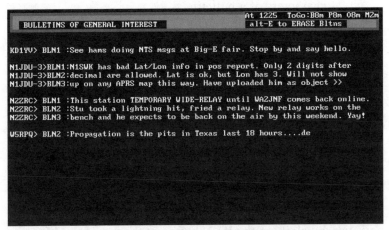

Figure 4-9—The bulletin window in APRS (DOS) *lists bulletins received by your station.*

station. The bulletins are color-coded dark blue to differentiate them from messages sent and received by your station. (Figure 4-8 illustrates the *WinAPRS* Message List window, which is very similar to the *MacAPRS* Message List window.)

pocketAPRS

To read a bulletin from another station with *pocketAPRS:*
1. Tap the MENU icon on the Palm III.
2. Select Messages from the Views menu.
3. Select Bulletins from the pick list at the top of the Messages window.

TH-D7

To read a bulletin from another station with the TH-D7:
1. Press the **MSG** button.
2. Press the **up** or **down** button so that the cursor appears next to LIST, then press the **OK** button.
3. Press the **up** or **down** button to scroll through the list of received messages. (The TH-D7 stores the last 16 received messages.)
4. When you have located the bulletin you wish to read, press the **OK** button when you are ready to read the second half of the message. (The TH-D7 initially displays the first 24 characters of a bulletin. Pressing **OK** reveals the second 24 characters of a bulletin.
5. When you are finished reading the bulletin, press the **ESC** button twice.

WinAPRS

To read bulletins with *WinAPRS*, select **Message List** from the Lists menu and the Message List window appears containing all the bulletins sent and received by your station. The bulletins are colored dark blue to differentiate them from messages sent and received by your station. (Figure 4-8 illustrates the *WinAPRS* Message List window.)

By default the *WinAPRS* Message List displays all the messages and bulletins sent and received by your station, however, by clicking the **BLN** button at the top of the Message List window, the window only displays bulletins. Clicking the

All button causes the Message List to return to its default, that is, displaying all messages and bulletins.

Adding Objects To Maps

Besides your APRS station, you can add other things to the APRS map and they will appear on all the APRS maps in your network. For example, you can display the path of a hurricane, the lead runner in a marathon, the lead vehicle in a parade, or a mobile communications control center in an emergency or natural disaster scenario.

Let us use the hurricane example. Hurricane Hiram is coming up the coast. You obtain its coordinates, speed and course from the National Weather Service, the Weather Channel or some other reliable source. With this information in hand, you access the add object function of APRS, and input the name, coordinates, speed and course of the hurricane. You also select an appropriate icon for the APRS map display (enter the @ in order to display the hurricane icon). (**Figure 4-10** illustrates an object, Hurricane Hiram, that an APRS user placed on a map.)

As you receive updates concerning the position, speed and

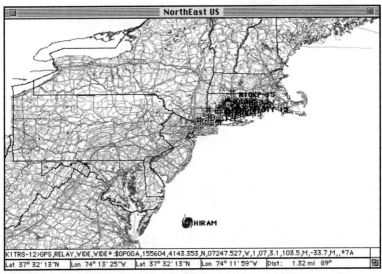

Figure 4-10—The icon of Hurricane Hiram moving up the East Coast is under the control of an APRS station operator.

course of Hurricane Hiram, you access APRS and enter the updated information in order to adjust the icon of the hurricane on the APRS map. And, when the hurricane is over, you access APRS to remove the hurricane icon from the APRS map.

The following describes how to add or delete an object on an APRS map with each version of APRS. It also describes how to change the position of an object on an APRS map.

APRS (DOS)

To add an object to an APRS map with *APRS (DOS)*:
1. Press **I** (for Input), then press **A** (for Add).
2. When prompted, type the requested information concerning the object. (The current position of your cursor on the map is the latitude and longitude displayed in the prompt.)

To change the position of an object on a map with *APRS (DOS)*:
1. Move the cursor to the icon of the object on the APRS map.
2. Press **Enter**.
3. Move the cursor to the new location of the object on the APRS map.
4. Press **Insert**.

To delete an object from an APRS map with *APRS (DOS)*:
1. Press **P** (for Positions).
2. Move the cursor to the object you wish to delete.
3. Press **Enter**.
4. Press **D** (for Delete).
5. Press **Y** (for Yes) to delete the object from the maps of the other APRS stations on frequency.

APRS+SA

To add an object to a *Street Atlas* map with *APRS+SA*:
1. Select a Create Object... command from the Object menu.
- Create Object from Map adds an object positioned at the upper right corner of the current *Street Atlas* map display.
- Create Object Manually adds an object positioned at the location that you specify.
- Create Object at My Current Location adds an object positioned at the same location as your station.
2. When the Object Editor window appears, type and select the parameters of the object you wish to add.

- If you selected the Create Object from Map command, click on the **Map** button to obtain the latitude and longitude of the upper right corner of the current *Street Atlas* map display.
- If you selected the Create Object at My Current Location command, the latitude, longitude, and icon displayed in the Object Editor window represent the position and icon of your station.

3. Click on the **OK** button.
4. Click on the **Close** button.

To delete an object from a Street Atlas map with *APRS+SA*:

1. Click on the **Objects** tab.
2. When the list of objects appears, click on the object you wish to delete with the right mouse button.
3. Select State, then select **Kill from the State** sub-menu.

MacAPRS

To add an object to an APRS map with *MacAPRS*:

1. Select **Edit/Add Station/Object...** from the Edit menu or type **Command-E**.
2. Type and select the parameters of the object you wish to add in the Add Object or Station window. (The latitude and longitude displayed in the Latitude: and Longitude: boxes is the current position of your cursor on the map.)
3. Click on the **OK** button.

To change the position of an object on an APRS map with *MacAPRS*:

1. Click on the icon for the object on the APRS map.
2. Select **Edit/Add Station/Object...** from the Edit menu or type **Command-E**.
3. *Enter* and select the parameters of the object you wish to change in the Add Object or Station window.
4. Click on the **OK** button.

To delete an object from an APRS map with *MacAPRS*:

1. Select Station List from the Lists menu.
2. When the Station List appears, select the object you wish to delete from the list.
3. Press **Delete**.
4. Close the Station List window.
5. Select **Clear/Redraw** from the Display menu or type **Command-L**.

pocketAPRS

To add an object to a map with *pocketAPRS*:

1. Tap on the MENU icon on the Palm III.
2. Select Map from the Views menu.
3. Tap the cross (+) icon at the bottom of the map window.
4. Tap the location on the map where you want to add the object.
5. When the Objects window appears, enter and select the parameters of the object.
6. Tap the **Done** button.

Another way to add an object is to select **Add Object** from the Main menu, then enter and select the parameters of the object in the Objects window.

To delete an object from a map with *pocketAPRS*:

1. Tap on the MENU icon on the Palm III.
2. Select **Map** from the Views menu.
3. Tap the arrow icon at the bottom of the map window.
4. Tap the object you wish to delete.
5. Select **Delete** from the drop-down menu.

WinAPRS

To add an object to an APRS map with *WinAPRS*:

1. Move your cursor to the approximate map location of the object you are adding.
2. From the Edit menu, select **Edit/Add Weather Object...** for weather objects or **Edit/Add Station/Object...** for other objects.
3. Type and select the parameters of the object you wish to add in the Add Object window. (The latitude and longitude displayed in the Latitude: and Longitude: fields is the current position of your cursor on the map.)
3. Click on the **OK** button.

To change the position of an object on an APRS map with *WinAPRS*:

1. Click on the icon of the object on the APRS map.
2. From the Edit menu, select **Edit/Add Weather Object...** for weather objects or **Edit/Add Station/Object...** for other objects.
3. Enter and select the parameters of the object you wish to change in the Add Object window.
4. Click on **OK** button.

To delete an object from an APRS map with *WinAPRS*:

1. Select Station List from the Lists menu.
2. When the Station List appears, select the object you wish to delete from the list.
3. Press **Backspace**.
4. Close the Station List window.

Direction Finding

Direction finding is the process of locating the source of an unknown radio signal. Direction finding is essential when that unknown radio signal is causing interference, intentional or unintentional, to other radio stations.

Traditionally, direction finding was an acquired art demanding a lot of practice and patience, as well as some specialized equipment. APRS has lessened this burden and permits more stations to participate in direction finding. Even stations that lack directional antennas can participate in the hunt just like their beam-equipped ham radio brethren.

Omnidirectional Direction Finding

In the past, there was one requirement that no station could ignore in order to participate in direction finding: the need for a directional antenna and the ability to move that antenna to obtain a bearing on the unknown radio signal that was the object of the hunt. Now, *APRS (DOS)* permits groups and individual stations equipped with *omnidirectional* antennas to participate in the hunt.

Group Omnidirectional Direction Finding

The following describes how to use *APRS (DOS)* for *omnidirectional* direction finding with a group of stations.

1. Each APRS station participating in the hunt should monitor the channel on which the unknown radio signal is transmitting.
2. Each APRS station should enter the signal strength of the unknown radio signal into *APRS (DOS)*. If a station does not detect any signal, this information is also valuable and should be entered into *APRS (DOS)*. To enter the signal strength of the unknown radio signal:
   a. Press **I** (for Input), then press **D** (for DF).
   b. Press **0** (zero). Next, type the relative signal strength (1 to 9) of the unknown radio signal or press **0** (zero) if you

detect no signal. Use the following table for entering the relative signal strength (RSS):

RSS	Description
0	No signal detected
1	Barely detectable signal
2	Detectable signal, but extremely weak and unreadable
3	Weak and barely readable signal
4	Noisy, but readable signal
5	Readable signal, but with some noise
6	Good signal, but with detectable noise
7	Very good signal with very little detectable noise
8	Strong signal with no detectable noise
9	Very strong signal (with no detectable noise)

3. Each APRS station (or one or two designated stations) should check the local voice repeaters seeking omnidirectional signal reports from any stations wishing to assist in the hunt.

4. Each voice station that assists in the hunt must be entered into APRS. In addition to the signal strength reported by each voice station, you also need its location, height above average terrain (HAAT), antenna gain, and the compass direction (in degrees) that their antenna favors, if any. To enter this information:

a. Type **I** (for Input), then type **A** (for Add).

b. When prompted, type the requested information concerning the voice station. (The current position of your cursor on the map is the latitude and longitude displayed in the Latitude and Longitude prompts.) Be sure to press **D** (for DF) at the Symbols prompt, **0** (zero) at the DF Bearing prompt, and the signal strength of the unknown station as reported by the voice station at the Relative Signal Strength prompt. If no signal is detected by the voice station, press **0** (zero) at the Relative Signal Strength prompt.

5. Press **M** (for Maps), then press **P** (for Plots), **D** (for DF) and **O** (for Omnidirectional). APRS plots the relative signal strength data on the map in a manner that helps to pinpoint the source of the unknown radio signal.

First, APRS plots the largest circles around those stations

that gave weakest signal reports. The weaker the signal report, the larger the circle because if the signal is weak, then it likely originates from a farther distance than if the signal is strong. The farther distance translates to a larger coverage circle.

After plotting the largest coverage circles, APRS plots continuously smaller circles representing continuously stronger signal reports. After plotting the smallest coverage circles, which represent the strongest signal reports, it plots gray-colored coverage circles that represent the coverage areas of stations that gave no signal reports, that is, the stations that could not hear any signal from the unknown station.

To interpret this display:

1. Eliminate the areas covered by the gray coverage circles. Nothing was heard in the gray coverage circles, so the unknown radio signal cannot be located within the grayed areas.

2. Locate the greatest concentration of non-gray circle intersections. The unknown radio signal is likely to be emanating from this area of the map.

Figure 4-11 illustrates a simple example of a group APRS

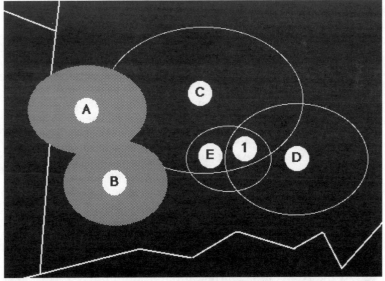

Figure 4-11—A simplified example showing how APRS displays the results of a group of stations using omnidirectional antennas for direction finding.

direction finding display. The coverage circles labeled A and B are gray and represent the areas where no signal was received. You can eliminate these gray areas as the possible source of the unknown radio signal.

Coverage circle C is the largest and represents the weakest signal report. Coverage circle E is the smallest and represents the strongest signal report. Coverage circle D falls somewhere in between C and E in size and signal strength. The area labeled 1 represents the greatest concentration of non-gray circle intersections. Area 1 is likely to be the source of the unknown radio signal.

Solo Omnidirectional Direction Finding

Using *APRS (DOS)* omnidirectional direction finding on an individual basis requires a different technique than that used for *omnidirectional* direction finding with a group. Instead of using signal strength and bearing information, the solo *omnidirectional* direction finding station must find the points where the unknown radio signal fades in or out. By plotting these fade points on an APRS map, you are able to locate the source of the unknown radio signal (at the center of the plotted fade points).

You must find and plot a minimum of three fade points for successful solo *omnidirectional* direction finding. To discover these points, monitor the unknown radio signal while traveling through the general area of its source. When the radio signal fades in or out, you have found a fade point and should enter it into APRS. (Fading in occurs as you travel into the coverage area of the unknown radio signal, whereas fading out occurs as you travel out of the coverage area.)

To narrow your search area, you may attenuate your receiver or tighten its squelch. As a result, the fade points occur closer to each other. Narrowing your search field is a good strategy to use after you have plotted a wide area search field with no attenuation and/or the squelch wide open.

To use *APRS (DOS)* for solo omnidirectional direction finding:

1. Press the **F5** key whenever you discover a fade point.
2. At the New Pass Configuration prompt, press **Y** (for Yes) for the first fade point entry and press **N** (for No) for subsequent fade point entries. Only press **Y** again if you

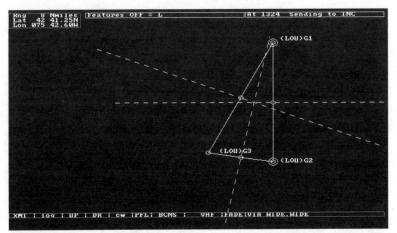

Figure 4-12—A simple example of a solo APRS direction finding display using three fade points.

change your radio configuration, e.g., you use a different antenna, attenuate your receiver, tighten the squelch, etc.

3. After entering three or more fade points, press **M** (for Maps), then press **P** (for Plots), and **F** (for Fade) to display the *APRS (DOS)* calculation of the location of the unknown radio signal. **Figure 4-12** illustrates the result of a solo APRS direction finding expedition using three fade points.

In this example, WA1LOU traveled south and began hearing the unknown radio signal at the fade point labeled (LOU)G1. Continuing to travel south, the unknown radio signal disappeared at fade point (LOU)G2. WA1LOU turned right and traveling west-northwest, reacquired the unknown radio signal at fade point (LOU)G3. The intersection of the three dotted bearing lines indicates the calculated position of the unknown radio signal based on the three fade points.

For a more accurate calculation of the location of the unknown radio signal source, you need more than three fade point entries. Notice how the calculated position shifts when WA1LOU enters a fourth fade point at (LOU)G4, as illustrated in **Figure 4-13**. The calculated location of the unknown radio signal is at the intersection of the two solid lines plotted between fade points G1-G3 and G2-G4.

Operation 4-27

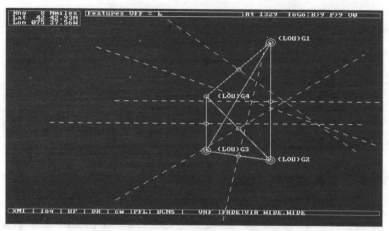

Figure 4-13—Entering additional fade points results in more accurate solo APRS direction finding.

Although additional points should improve the triangulation, they often just confuse the picture. It is best to use fade points in groups of three for each antenna configuration, then proceed with your best guess, add attenuation and begin a new pass configuration. Only the fade points discovered at each new pass configuration should be used with each other.

Directional Direction Finding

APRS supports traditional direction finding, that is, direction finding using beam antennas or specialized direction finding equipment such as a Doppler measuring device like the DFjr, which is a compact, Doppler-based direction finding system specifically designed for APRS operation. With a device like the DFjr and a GPS unit interfaced to your APRS station, you can enjoy automatically generated real time displays of direction finding vectors with all three versions of APRS.

Using beam antennas for direction finding requires more work. You must manually enter the beam headings of the unknown radio signal into APRS.

APRS (DOS)

To enter a beam heading into *APRS (DOS)*:
1. Press **I** (for Inputs), then press **D** (for DF).

2. At the DF Bearing prompt, type the beam heading (in degrees) of the unknown radio signal (use 360 for 0 degrees north).

3. At the Enter Quality prompt, type a value between 1 and 8 (8 being the best) for the quality of the unknown radio signal.

After entering the information requested by APRS, the program draws a yellow line on the map representing the beam heading you entered. A solid line indicates a good quality signal. Dotted lines indicate lesser quality signals. Other APRS stations that are hunting for the source of the unknown radio signal should also enter their beam headings and APRS displays them on the map, too.

Non-APRS stations may also join in the hunt. To add a non-APRS station beam heading report to the map:

1. Press **I** (for Input), then press **A** (for Add).

2. When prompted, enter the requested information concerning the non-APRS station. (The current position of your cursor on the map is the latitude and longitude displayed in the Latitude and Longitude prompts.) Be sure to press **D** (for DF) at the Symbols prompt, the reported beam heading at the DF Bearing prompt (use 360 for 0 degrees north), and the quality of the unknown radio signal at the Enter Quality prompt.

Figure 4-14 illustrates the result of the manual entry of beam headings. In this example, APRS station WA1LOU-15

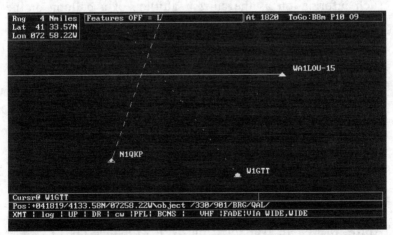

Figure 4-14—APRS (DOS) displays the manually-entered beam headings of three stations attempting to find the source of an unknown radio signal.

entered a beam heading of 270 degrees with a signal quality of 8. Non-APRS stations N1QKP and W1GTT respectively reported beam headings of 15 and 330 degrees and signal quality estimates of 4 and 1. WA1LOU entered their reports and Figure 4-14 is the result. The source of the unknown radio signal likely resides near the center of the triangle formed by the three beam headings.

pocketAPRS

To enter a beam heading in *pocketAPRS*:
1. Tap the MENU icon on the Palm III.
2. Select Manual DF Report from the Main menu.
3. Move the stylus around the compass dial to select the beam heading. (Your selection appears in the lower half of the compass dial.)
4. Tap the **Local** button to plot the heading on your map only or tap the **Active** button to create an active object that is transmitted to the APRS network.

Telemetry

APRS is able to receive and display telemetry from diverse moving objects such as balloons aloft and animals in the wild. The telemetry can be diverse, too. For example, it may include such information as the current altitude of a balloon or the current body temperature of an animal. GPS can also be used to provide position information of these moving objects.

The key to monitoring telemetry with APRS is the Micro Interface Module (MIM), which is a complete telemetry TNC in one integrated circuit. MIM has five analog and eight digital inputs, which may be sampled at a user-selectable time period. Each sample is output in a standard AX.25 packet. Telemetry sensors on the MIM input, a transmitter on the MIM output, and a battery are all you need to complete the package (GPS can be used optionally as an input).

(Carl Wick, N3MIM, developed the MIM and he worked with Will Clement, N3XLM, to massage MIM for APRS. MIMs are available from APRS Engineering LLC, 115 Old Farm Ct, Glen Burnie, MD 21060, 410-553-6021, email **bruninga@nadn.navy.mil**.)

Initializing a Telemetry Scenario

MIM telemetry transmissions consist of packets containing a string of data that represents each sampling of its inputs. Any station can receive these packets, but the data contained in these packets is meaningless.

In order to make this data meaningful, a designated APRS station must set the stage for the telemetry scenario. This is accomplished by sending four messages over the APRS network. The first message defines the telemetry labels, the second message defines the telemetry units, the third message defines the telemetry equations, and the fourth message defines the digital bit definitions and the project name.

Stations wishing to receive meaningful telemetry must receive the four messages. If they do, their APRS software extracts information from these messages in order to display received telemetry in a meaningful manner. (**Figure 4-15** shows the *APRS (DOS)* Telemetry window displaying the following information concerning a balloon launch: altitude, temperature, pressure, and battery measurements.)

APRS (DOS)

To initialize a telemetry scenario with *APRS (DOS)*:
1. Press **S** (for Send).

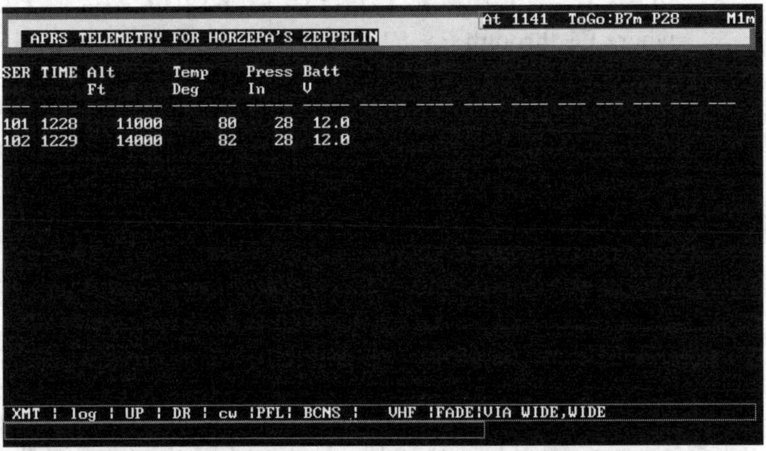

Figure 4-15—The **APRS (DOS)** *Telemetry window displays telemetry data received over the air.*

2. At the To: prompt, type the call sign of the MIM.
3. At the Entr MsgText: prompt, type the telemetry labels. The format for the telemetry labels is PARM.P1,P2,P3,P4,P5,B1,B2,B3,B4,B5,B6,B7, where P1 through P5 and B1 through B7 are the parameter names (for example, PARM.Alt,Temp,Press,Batt). The maximum length of each parameter is 9 characters for P1, 8 characters for P2, 6 each for P3 through P5, 5 each for B1 through B3, and 4 each for B4 through B7.
4. Press **S** again.
5. At the To: prompt, type the call sign of the MIM.
6. At the Entr MsgText: prompt, type the telemetry units. The format for the telemetry units is UNIT.C1,C2,C3,C4,C5,D1,D2,D3,D4,D5,D6,D7, where C1 through C5 are the units for analog ports and D1 through D7 are the labels for the bits (for example, UNIT.Ft,Deg,In,V). The maximum length of each unit is 9 characters for C1, 8 characters for C2, 6 each for C3 through C5, 5 each for D1 through D3, and 4 each for D4 through D7.
7. Press **S** again.
8. At the To: prompt, type the call sign of the MIM.
9. At the Entr MsgText: prompt, enter the telemetry equations. The format for the telemetry equations is EQNS.E1,F1,G1,E2,F2,G2,E3,F3,G3,E4,F4,G4,E5,F5,G5 where E1 through E5, F1 through F5, and G1 through G5 are the coefficients of a quadratic equation for each of the five analog channels (for example, EQNS.0.53,0,0,0). The quadratic equation is $H = E*J\verb|^|2 + F*J + G$ where H is the final value and J is the value transmitted by the MIM.
10. Press **S** again.
11. At the To: prompt, type the call sign of the MIM.
12. At the Entr MsgText: prompt, enter the digital bit definitions and the project name.

The format for the digital bit definitions and the project name is BITS.KKKKKKKK,L where KKKKKKKK indicates whether the on-state of each of the digital inputs is represented by a 0 or 1 and where L is the name of the project up to 23 characters in length (for example,

BITS.10110000,Horzepa's Zeppelin).

13. Stop when you are finished entering the fourth message.

MacAPRS

To initialize a telemetry scenario with *MacAPRS*:

1. Select New Message... from the Lists menu or type **Command-M**.

2. In the To: field, type the call sign of the MIM.

3. Press **TAB**, then type the telemetry labels in the Msg: field. The format for the telemetry labels is PARM.P1,P2,P3,P4,P5,B1,B2,B3,B4,B5,B6,B7, where P1 through P5 and B1 through B7 are the parameter names (for example, PARM.Alt,Temp,Press,Batt). The maximum length of each parameter is 9 characters for P1, 8 characters for P2, 6 each for P3 through P5, 5 each for B1 through B3, and 4 each for B4 through B7.

4. Click on the **OK** button.

5. Select New Message... from the Lists menu or type **Command-M**.

6. In the To: field, type the call sign of the MIM.

7. Press **TAB**, then type the telemetry units in the Msg: field. The format for the telemetry units is UNIT.C1,C2,C3,C4,C5,D1,D2,D3,D4,D5,D6,D7, where C1 through C5 are the units for analog ports and D1 through D7 are the labels for the bits (for example, UNIT.Ft,Deg,In,V). The maximum length of each unit is 9 characters for C1, 8 characters for C2, 6 each for C3 through C5, 5 each for D1 through D3, and 4 each for D4 through D7.

8. Click on the **OK** button.

9. Select New Message... from the Lists menu or type **Command-M**.

10. In the To: field, type the call sign of the MIM.

11. Press **TAB**, then type the telemetry equations in the Msg: field.

The format for the telemetry equations is EQNS.E1,F1,G1,E2,F2,G2,E3,F3,G3,E4,F4,G4,E5,F5,G5 where E1 through E5, F1 through F5, and G1 through G5 are the coefficients of a quadratic equation for each of the five analog channels (for example, EQNS.0.53,0,0,0). The quadratic equation is $H = E*J^2 + F*J + G$ where H is the final value and J is the value transmitted by the MIM.

12. Click on the **OK** button.
13. Select New Message... from the Lists menu or type **Command-M**.
14. In the To: field, type the call sign of the MIM.
15. Press **TAB**, then type the digital bit definitions in the Msg: field.

    The format for the digital bit definitions and the project name is BITS.KKKKKKKK,L where KKKKKKKK indicates whether the on-state of each of the digital inputs is represented by a 0 or 1 and where L is the name of the project up to 23 characters in length (for example, BITS.10110000,Horzepa's Zeppelin).

16. Click on the **OK** button.

Displaying Telemetry

The following describes how to display received telemetry.

APRS (DOS)

To display received telemetry with *APRS (DOS)*, press **L** (for List), then **T** (for Telemetry).

The Telemetry display appears (similar to the window illustrated in Figure 4-15) and displays any telemetry packets you may have received. If your station has received the four messages intended to set up the telemetry values, then the display will be appropriately modified to those values and labels. Otherwise, the data will be displayed in the raw count form.

The SER and TIME fields appear in all Telemetry list windows. The other fields, including the name of the project (in this example, Horzepa's Zeppelin), are dependent on the contents of the messages transmitted by the station designated to initialize the telemetry scenario. SER and TIME indicate a sequential number assigned to each telemetry packet and time each packet was received from the MIM.

APRS+SA

To display received telemetry with *APRS+SA*, click on the **Telemetry** tab.

APRS Data

There is a wealth of information that you may get from APRS in addition to what the book has already described. This data usually appears in a list, however, some of it appears graphically. The following descriptions highlight some of the more important data that you can access with APRS.

In addition to presenting a map, APRS maps display other information usually related to what is happening on the displayed map, for example, some versions of APRS display the last packet received by your APRS station in the lower portion of the APRS screen.

The bottom of the screen in *APRS (DOS)* also displays the keys to press in order to display screens containing other information. These keys are **A, B, D, H, L, P, V, Alt-T** and **F1** for All beacons, Bulletins, Digipeaters used, Heard log, Latest beacons, Positions, View all packets, Telemetry and Help, respectively. The bottom of the screen also displays keys to press in order to display command menus. These keys are **,** for Controls, Files, Input, Map, Operations, Weather and Set-up, respectively.

Cursor Position

APRS (DOS)

In *APRS (DOS)*, the coordinates of the current position of the cursor on the map appear in the upper left corner of maps.

APRS+SA

With *APRS+SA*, the coordinates of the current position of the cursor on the Street Atlas map appear in the lower left corner of the map, unless the cursor is located on a map road feature (then, the name of the road appears in the lower left corner).

MacAPRS

In *MacAPRS*, the coordinates of the current position of the cursor on the map appear in the lower left corner of maps.

WinAPRS

In *WinAPRS*, The coordinates and grid square of the current position of the cursor on the map appear in the lower left of maps.

Station Data

All versions of APRS allow you to obtain information about the stations that are active on your APRS network.

APRS (DOS)

APRS (DOS) provide the following information concerning each station: call sign, day and time of reception, day and time of entry, latitude, longitude, course, speed, and contents of identification string, if any. (**Figure 4-16** illustrates the Positions window of *APRS (DOS)*.)

To view this information, type **P**.

APRS+SA

APRS+SA provides the call sign, day of the month and time of first reception, contents of identification string, digipeater path, and date and time of last reception.

To view this information, click on the Status tab.

MacAPRS

MacAPRS lists the stations received by your station in their order of receipt (the oldest first) and provide the following information concerning each station: primary and secondary map icons, call sign, the CAATOFPWDG field, number of

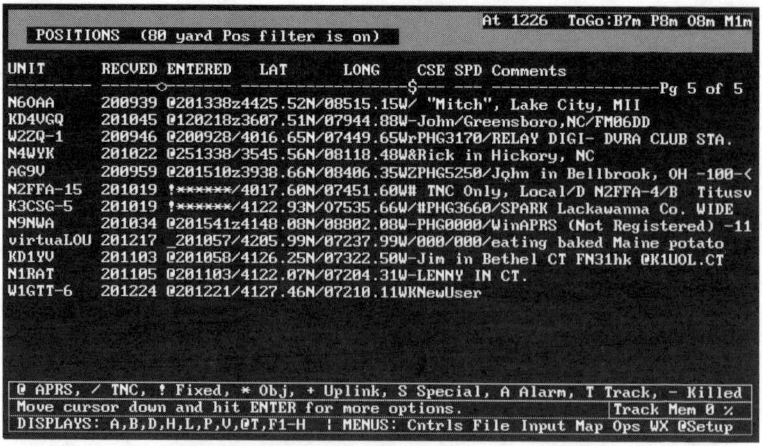

```
                                                      At 1226   ToGo:B7m P8m O8m M1m
     POSITIONS   (88 yard Pos filter is on)

UNIT        RECUED ENTERED    LAT      LONG     CSE SPD Comments
--------    ------o-------    --------------------o-----------------------Pg 5 of 5
N6OAA       200939 0201338z4425.52N/08515.15W/ "Mitch", Lake City, MII
KD4UGQ      201045 0120218z3607.51N/07944.88W-John/Greensboro,NC/FM06DD
W2ZQ-1      200946 0200928/4016.65N/07449.65WrPHG3170/RELAY DIGI- DVRA CLUB STA.
N4WYK       201022 0251338/3545.56N/08118.48W&Rick in Hickory, NC
AG9V        200959 0201510z3938.66N/08406.35WZPHG5258/Jqhn in Bellbrook, OH -100-<
N2FFA-15    201019 !******/4017.60N/07451.60W# TNC Only, Local/D N2FFA-4/B  Titusv
K3CSG-5     201019 !******/4122.93N/07535.66W/#PHG3660/SPARK Lackawanna Co. WIDE
N9NWA       201034 0201541z4148.00N/08802.08W-PHG0000/WinAPRS (Not Registered) -11
virtuaLOU   201217 _201057/4205.99N/07237.99W/000/000/eating baked Maine potato
KD1YV       201103 0201058/4126.25N/07322.50W-Jim in Bethel CT FN31hk @K1UOL.CT
N1RAT       201105 0201103/4122.07N/07204.31W-LENNY IN CT.
W1GTT-6     201224 0201221/4127.46N/07210.11WKNewUser



@ APRS, / TNC, ! Fixed, * Obj, + Uplink, S Special, A Alarm, T Track, - Killed
Move cursor down and hit ENTER for more options.              |Track Mem 0 %
DISPLAYS: A,B,D,H,L,P,V,@T,F1-H  ! MENUS: Cntrls File Input Map Ops WX @Setup
```

Figure 4-16—The Positions window of APRS (DOS) lists the APRS stations received by your station.

packets received, time of first receipt, and contents of identification string (if any).

Each column of the CAATOFPWDG field indicates the following information concerning each station:

The C column indicates the icon character.

The first A column indicates the icon table.

The second A column indicates the alarm type, if any.

The T column indicates the tracked type, if any.

The O column indicates the object type, if any.

The F column indicates the flagged type, if any.

The **P** column indicates the current count of the message pending counter.

The W column indicates the warning type, if any.

The **D** column indicates the danger type, if any.

The G column indicates the GPS destination, if any.

To view this information, select Station List from the Lists menu.

To view this information, select Station List from the Lists menu or type **Command-1**. (**Figure 4-17** illustrates the Station Lists window of *WinAPRS*, which is very similar to the Station Lists window of *MacAPRS*.)

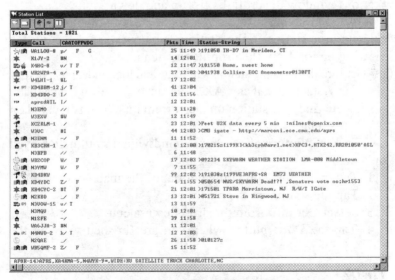

Figure 4-17—The Station List of **WinAPRS** *delineates the APRS stations received by your station.*

You can also obtain information about an individual station in *MacAPRS*, by double-clicking on the map icon of the station. A window appears telling you all about that station.

pocketAPRS

To view station information in *pocketAPRS*:
1. Tap the MENU icon on the Palm III.
2. Select Station List from the Views menu.
3. Select the type of station data you wish to view from the pick list at the top of the Stations window:
• Position displays the longitude and latitude of each station.
• Status displays the status text, if any, of each station.
• Data displays the posit text, if any, of each station.
• Distance displays the distance (miles) and direction (degrees) of each station relative to the location of your station.
• Heard displays the date and time each station was first received by your station and graphically indicates the number of packets received from each station
• Digi Path displays the digipeater path of each station.
• Alerts displays any alarms related to each station.

Tap the up and down arrows at the lower right of the Stations window to scroll the list up and down.

You can obtain information about an individual station by selecting the station in the Stations window, then selecting the viewing option from the drop-down menu.
• Get Info displays the station's latitude and longitude, posit text, if any, status text, if any, AX.25 destination, and digipeater path.
• Locate finds the station on the current map (if it is located on that map).

To obtain information about an individual station displayed on a map:
1. Tap the arrow icon at the bottom of the map window.
2. Tap the station on the map.
3. Select Get Info from the drop-down menu.
4. Tap the **Done** button when you are finished viewing the information.

TH-D7

The TH-D7 allows you to view information about the last 40

stations that the radio has received. When the forty-first station is received, the TH-D7 deletes the information concerning the first/oldest station received.

To view received station information with the TH-D7:

1. Press the **LIST** button.
2. Press the **up** and **down** buttons to scroll through the list of received stations. (The last/most recent station received is at the top of the list.)
3. When you have located the received station you wish to view, you may press the **OK** button to page through four screens of information concerning the selected station.

- The first screen displays the first 20 characters of the status text of the received station.
- The second screen displays the grid square of the received station, its map icon, its distance from the TH-D7, and the approximate compass direction of its location relative to the TH-D7. (This information is calculated using the TH-D7 position as determined by a GPS receiver connected to the TH-D7 or by the position information stored manually in the TH-D7 via the MENU-2-3 configuration command.)

If the map icon of the received station is not one of the 15 that the TH-D7 can display, then the alphanumeric characters representing the icon are displayed instead. The compass direction is indicated by a compass icon, which displays the approximate direction in 45-degree increments (straight up in 0 degrees or North; straight down is 180 degrees or South).

- The third screen displays the latitude and longitude of the received station.
- The contents of the fourth screen varies depending on the type of APRS station that has been received.

For mobile stations, the fourth screen displays the position comment, if any, and the course ("cse" in degrees) and speed ("s" in miles or kilometers) of the station.

For fixed stations with Power-Height-Gain-Direction (PHGD) data appended to their packets, the fourth screen displays the transmit power ("pw" in watts), antenna height ("h" in feet), antenna gain ("ant" in dB), and the compass direction that the antenna favors ("d" in degrees). If the antenna is nondirectional, the d field contains "omni."

For fixed stations without Power-Height-Gain-Direction (PHGD) data appended to their packets, the fourth screen displays blank course (cse) and speed (s) fields.

For fixed stations using compressed data, the fourth screen displays the radius of the station's coverage area in miles.

For weather stations, the fourth screen displays wind direction ("dir" in degrees), wind speed ("s" in miles or kilometers per hour), air temperature ("t" in degrees Fahrenheit or Celsius), and the amount of rainfall ("r" in inches or millimeters) measured during the past hour.

For objects with course and speed data included in their packets, the fourth screen displays the course ("cse" in degrees) and speed ("s" in miles or kilometers) of the object and the call sign of the station that transmitted the object.

For objects without course and speed data included in their packets, the fourth screen displays the call sign of the station that transmitted the object.

4. When you are finished viewing the station information, press the **ESC** button as many times as necessary (2 to 5 times) to exit the List screens.

WinAPRS

WinAPRS lists the stations received by your station in their order of receipt (the oldest first) and provide the following information concerning each station: primary and secondary map icons, call sign, the CAATOFPWDG field, number of packets received, time of first receipt, and contents of identification string (if any).

Each column of the CAATOFPWDG field indicates the following information concerning each station:

The C column indicates the icon character.

The first A column indicates the icon table.

The second A column indicates the alarm type, if any.

The T column indicates the tracked type, if any.

The O column indicates the object type, if any.

The F column indicates the flagged type, if any.

The P column indicates the current count of the message pending counter.

The W column indicates the warning type, if any.

The D column indicates the danger type, if any.

The G column indicates the GPS destination, if any.

To view this information, select Station List from the Lists menu. (Figure 4-17 illustrates the Station Lists window of *WinAPRS*, which is very similar to the Station Lists window of *MacAPRS*.)

You can also obtain information about an individual station in *WinAPRS*, by double-clicking on the map icon of the station. A window appears telling you all about that station.

Digipeater List

All versions of APRS provide a way of viewing the digipeater path of the APRS stations received by your station.

APRS (DOS)

APRS (DOS) allows you to obtain a list of the digipeaters used by each APRS station received by your station. The list includes the call sign and digipeater path of each station. An asterisk (*) next to the call sign indicates that you received the packets directly from that station, not via a digipeater. An asterisk next to a digipeater indicates that you received the station from that digipeater. Press **D** (for Digipeater) to display the Digipeater List. (**Figure 4-18** illustrates the Digipeater List of *APRS (DOS)*.)

```
   DIGIPEATERS USED (raw packet headers)

*FROM      >TO..,DIGI-1,DIGI-2*,DIGI-3....:    (* shows last digi heard by you)
--------------⬥-----------------------------------------------------Pg 6 of 6
 N9NWA     >APRSW,GATE,GATE,WIDE*:
 W4VRP     >APRS,KA30DJ-8,WIDE*:
 AA8JK-10  >ID,GATE*,WIDE:
 KD1YV     >APRS,N1FTW-15,WIDE,WIDE*,WIDE:
 N1RAT     >APRS,W1GTT-15*,WIDE:
*N1QKP-15  >APRS,RELAY,WIDE,WIDE:
*W1GTT-6   >APRS,W1GTT-15,WIDE,WIDE:
 WA1LOU-15>APRS,WIDE,WIDE*:
 KP4DDB    >APRS,GATE*,WIDE:




Move cursor down and hit ENTER for more options. !VIA WIDE,WIDE
DISPLAYS: A,B,D,H,L,P,V,@T,F1-H  ¦ MENUS: Cntrls File Input Map Ops WX @Setup
```

Figure 4-18—The Digipeater List of APRS (DOS) *lists the digipeaters used by the APRS stations received at your station.*

APRS+SA

To view this information, click on the Status or History tab and refer to the Path column.

MacAPRS

MacAPRS does not have a digipeater list function, however, if you double-click on the icon of a station on an APRS map, the software displays the digipeater path used by that station.

pocketAPRS

pocketAPRS does not have a digipeater list function, however, you may view the digipeater path used by each station by:
1. Tap the MENU icon on the Palm III.
2. Select Station List from the Views menu.
3. Select Digi Path from the pick list at the top of the Stations window.

WinAPRS

Although *WinAPRS* does not have a digipeater list function, if you double-click on the icon of a station on an APRS map, the software displays the digipeater information concerning that station.

```
                                              At 1228   ToGo:B6m P6m O6m M7m
      HEARD LOG (per hour for last 24 hrs)            Use F1 for HELP

Time(Hrs) 12 11 10  9  8
---------o------------------------------------------------------------Pg 6 of 6
N9NWA       .  .  1  .  .
W4URP       .  .  1  .  .
AA8JK-10    1  .  1  .  .
KD1YV       .  1  .  .  .
N1RAT       .  1  .  .  .
N1QKP-15    .  1  .  .  .
W1GTT-6     1 10  .  .  .
WA1LOU-15   1  .  .  .  .
KP4DDB      1  .  .  .  .




 Move cursor down and hit ENTER for more options.
 ID: N1QKP-15>ID,RELAY,WIDE,WIDE*:N1QKP-15/R RELAY/D N1QKP-1/B WIDE/N
```

Figure 4-19—The Heard Log of APRS (DOS) *lists the number of packets received each hour in a tabular format.*

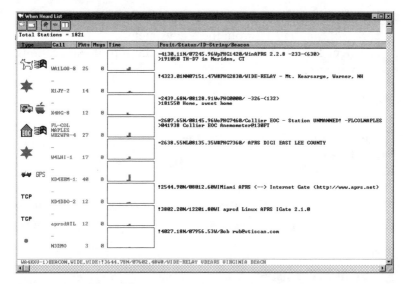

Figure 4-20—The When Heard List of MacAPRS lists the number of packets received each hour graphically.

Heard List

Some versions of APRS have a function that lists the number of packets received per hour from each station over the previous 24-hour period. *APRS (DOS)* presents this data in a tabular format, while *MacAPRS* and *WinAPRS* present this data graphically. (**Figures 4-19** and **4-20** illustrate the *APRS (DOS)* and *WinAPRS* versions of the display, respectively. The *MacAPRS* version of this display is very similar to the *WinAPRS* version.)

The following describes how to obtain the Heard List with each version of APRS.

APRS (DOS)

Press **H** (for Heard) to view the heard log in *APRS (DOS)*.

MacAPRS

To view this information, select When Heard from the Lists menu.

pocketAPRS

To view this information:

1. Tap the MENU icon on the Palm III.
2. Select Station List from the Views menu.
3. Select Heard from the pick list at the top of the Stations window.

WinAPRS

To view this information, select When Heard from the Lists menu. (Figure 4-20 illustrates the *WinAPRS* versions of the When Heard List.)

Weather Data

Most versions of APRS allow you to view weather data received from APRS weather stations.

APRS (DOS)

To display a list of weather stations in *APRS (DOS)*:
1. Press **P** (for Positions).
2. Press **J** (for Just), then press **W** (for Weather).

Press **N** (for Next weather station) at any time to sequentially display each weather station in the Weather window at the top of the screen.

To display weather stations on an *APRS (DOS)* map, press **J** (for Just), then press **W** (for Weather). By pressing **W** (for Weather), then **D** (for Display), and finally **T** (for temperature), **W** (for wind), **R** (for rainfall), or **B** (for barometric pressure), *APRS (DOS)* replaces the call signs of the weather stations on the APRS map with the temperature, wind, rainfall, or barometric pressure information, respectively. The line extending from the icon of a weather station indicates the direction of the wind.

APRS+SA

APRS+SA displays the following information regarding received APRS weather station data: call sign of weather station, latitude and longitude of station, wind direction (degrees), wind speed (mph), air temperature (degrees Fahrenheit), rainfall during previous hour (0.01 in), rainfall during previous day (0.01 in), atmospheric pressure (millibars), relative humidity (%), wind gust during previous 5 minutes (mph), day of month and time of report, type of weather station equipment, digipeater path, date and time of report.

To view this information, click on the **Weather** tab.

MacAPRS

MacAPRS permits you to receive weather information from the APRS weather stations received by your station in their order of receipt (the oldest first). The Weather List includes the following information concerning each station: primary and secondary map icon, call sign, time of last packet received, temperature (degrees Fahrenheit), rainfall during previous hour (0.01 in), rainfall during previous day (0.01 in), relative humidity (%), atmospheric pressure (millibars), wind speed (mph, wind gusts (mph), wind direction (degrees), number of alarms generated by the station, Weather List stations distance from your station (miles), and brand of weather station equipment. (**Figure 4-21** illustrates the Weather List window of *WinAPRS*, which is very similar to the Weather List window of *MacAPRS*.)

To view this information, select Weather List from the Lists menu or type **Command-3**.

MacAPRS also has a Weather Data function that displays

Weather List

Total Stations = 248

Type	Call	Day/Time	Temp	rRain	pRain	Humid	Pres		Wind	Gust	Dir	Dist	Alrm	Brand
	UB2VPA-4	19/11:57	82	0.00	0.00	73	1017	–	0	6	126	1183	0	AU
	KC2KLM-1	19/12:01	50	2.14	0.00	0	1030	–	0	0	358	101	0	U2k
	UB2COP	19/11:43	49	0.00	0.00	67	1030	–	5	16	104	0	U2k
	M3VMW	19/11:55	50	0.00	0.00	1	1030	–	0	4	100	179	0	U2k
	KD4DKW	19/12:01	61	1.16	0.00	0	1022	–	0	0	21	835	0	U2k
	M2KBD	19/11:56	47	0.00	0.00	67	1028	–	0	0	271	81	0	U2k
	M2QAE	19/11:58	45	0.00	0.00	0	0		0	0	67	115	0	UII
	AA3JY-3	19/11:53	76	0.00	0.00	0	0		0	0	222	162	0	U2k
	W8EH	19/12:01	52	0.00	0.00	0	0		0	2	315	628	0	UII
	K4LK	19/11:57	82	0.00	0.00	72	1018	–	3	4	97	1107	0	U2k
	KC8LCP-10	19/12:00	50	1.14	0.00	0	0		3	3	219	700	0	U2k
	N0BKB	19/12:00	44	0.00	0.03	0	0		5	11	337	1123	0	UII
	K4ROK	19/12:00	81	0.00	0.00	0	1029	–	0	0	295	488	0	U2k
	N8AGB	19/11:54	50	0.00	0.00	82	1013	+	0	0	358	624	0	U2k
	XC7YDU	19/10:48	56	0.00	0.00	0	0		0	0	0	2246	0	UII
	KP4KUL	19/11:57	79	0.00	0.00	74	1010	–	5	6	87	1101	0	
	N8HQP	19/11:59	50	0.00	0.00	61	1024	+	0	0	42	627	0	U2k
	U8GUC	19/12:00	54	0.00	0.00	43	1023		0	5	328	615	0	BSW
	MD8MS	19/11:58	52	0.00	0.00	0	0		0	0	360	621	0	UII
	U2LU	19/12:00	46	1.90	0.00	56	1028	+	0	0	171	106	0	U2k
	KP0ZH	19/11:48	44	0.00	0.01	86	1022	+	9	10	331	1071	0	U2k
	KA8FGE-11	19/11:54	50	7.90	0.00	73	1023	+	0	0	279	619	0	U2k
	KG9AE	19/11:50	50	0.00	0.00	87	1025	+	0	0	182	722	0	U2k
	KD4TWB	19/12:01	81	0.00	0.00	78	1018	–	0	2	167	1017	0	DAU
	KE4LKQ-1	19/12:00	48	0.00	0.00	14	1043	–	0	0	296	376	0	U2k
	AA6JR	19/12:00	61	0.00	0.00	0	1018	+	0	0	0	2589	0	U2k
	UA6YLD-4	19/11:58	64	0.00	0.00	0	0		0	26	98	2481	0	U2k
	KC8LCP-11	19/12:00	50	0.00	0.00	0	0		4	4	157	698	0	UII

N7LP-14>GPS,W7MOI-1*,WIDES-4:$GPRMC,160152,A,3320.92,N,11158.07,W,000.0,147.0,191099,012.3,E*6C

Figure 4-21—The Weather List of WinAPRS *delineates the weather data received from the APRS weather stations.*

weather data with the weather stations that appear on the APRS map. The weather data includes temperature, wind speed (mph), wind gusts (mph), rainfall (0.01 in), atmospheric pressure (millibars), relative humidity (%), and dewpoint. The line overlaid on the weather station icon indicates the direction of the wind. A counter indicates the age of the data (in minutes).

To view this information, select Station Display Mode from the Display, then select Weather Stations Only.

TH-D7

The TH-D7 allows you to view weather data received from APRS weather stations that are among the last 40 stations that the radio has received. When the forty-first station is received, the TH-D7 deletes the information concerning the first/oldest station received.

To view weather data with the TH-D7:

1. Press the **LIST** button.
2. Press the **OK** button twice.
2. Press the **up** and **down** buttons to scroll through the list of received stations to locate a weather station, as indicated by the weather (WX) station icon.
3. When you have located a weather station you wish to view, may press the **OK** button to view the following weather data: wind direction ("dir" in degrees), wind speed ("s" in miles or kilometers per hour), air temperature ("t" in degrees Fahrenheit or Celsius), and the amount of rainfall ("r" in inches or millimeters) measured during the past hour.
4. When you are finished viewing the weather data, press the **ESC** button five times to exit the List screens.

WinAPRS

WinAPRS permits you to receive weather information from the APRS weather stations received by your station in their order of receipt (the oldest first). The Weather List includes the following information concerning each station: map icon, call sign, time of last packet received, air temperature (degrees Fahrenheit), rainfall during previous hour (0.01 in.), rainfall during previous day (0.01 in.), relative humidity (%), atmospheric pressure (millibars), wind speed (mph), wind gusts (mph), wind direction (degrees), number of alarms generated by the station, and the Weather List stations distance from your station (miles). (Figure 4-21 illustrates the Weather List window of *WinAPRS*.)

To view this information, select Weather List from the Lists menu.

WinAPRS also has a Weather Data function that displays weather data with the weather stations that appear on the APRS map. The weather data includes temperature (degrees Fahrenheit), wind speed (mph), wind gusts (mph), rainfall (0.01 in), atmospheric pressure (millibars), and relative humidity (%), and dewpoint. The line overlaid on the weather station icon indicates the direction of the wind. A counter indicates the age of the data (in minutes).

To view this information, select Weather Stations Only from the Display menu.

View Packets

All versions of APRS permit you to obtain a list of the packets received by your station. (**Figures 4-22** and **4-23**, respectively, illustrate the view packets displays of *APRS (DOS)* and *WinAPRS*. The *MacAPRS* display is very similar to the *WinAPRS* display.)

The following describes how to view packets with each version of APRS.

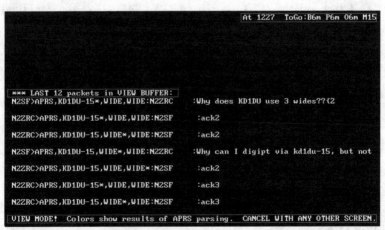

Figure 4-22—The View Packets list of **APRS (DOS)** *displays the last 12 packets received.*

Figure 4-23—The History List of WinAPRS lists all the packets received by your station.

APRS (DOS)

In *APRS (DOS)*, press **V** (for View) to view the packets received by your station.

APRS+SA

Click on the **TNC** tab in *APRS+SA* to list the received packets.

MacAPRS

With *MacAPRS*, select History List from the Lists menu or type **Command-5** to reveal the list of packets received by your station.

pocketAPRS

To view received packets in *pocketAPRS*, tap the MENU icon on the Palm III, then select View Packets from the Views menu.

WinAPRS

In *WinAPRS*, select History List from the Lists menu to view the list of received packets. (Figure 4-23 illustrates the *WinAPRS* History List.)

Flagged Station List

MacAPRS and *WinAPRS* permits you to display a list of the flagged stations received by your station in their order of receipt (the oldest first). The Flagged Station List includes the following information concerning each station: map icon, call sign, time of first receipt, number of packets received, distance from your station, version of *MacAPRS* and/or *WinAPRS* being used by the station, computer type, and contents of identification string (if any). (**Figure 4-24** illustrates the Flagged Station List of *WinAPRS*, which is very similar to the *MacAPRS* Flagged Station List.)

To obtain the Flagged Station List with *MacAPRS* and *WinAPRS*, select Flagged Station List from the Lists menu.

By the way, to flag stations in *MacAPRS*, select *MacAPRS* Settings... from the Settings menu and click on the **Auto Flag Macs** and/or **Auto Flag Windows** buttons, then click on the **OK** button.

To flag stations in *WinAPRS*, select *WinAPRS* from the Settings menu and click on the Auto Flag Macs and/or **Auto Flag**

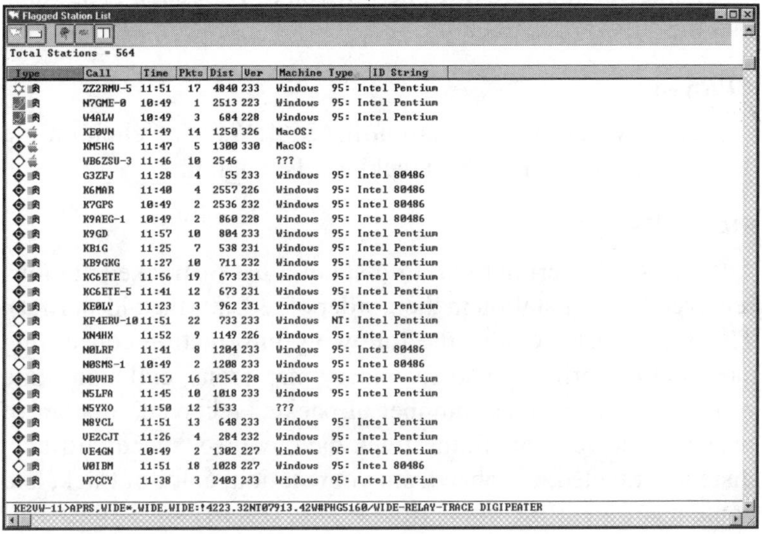

Type	Call	Time	Pkts	Dist	Ver	Machine Type	ID String
	ZZ2RMV-5	11:51	17	4840	233	Windows 95:	Intel Pentium
	N7GME-0	10:49	1	2513	223	Windows 95:	Intel Pentium
	W4ALW	10:49	3	684	228	Windows 95:	Intel Pentium
	KE0VN	11:49	14	1250	326	MacOS:	
	KM5HG	11:47	5	1300	330	MacOS:	
	WB6ZSU-3	11:46	10	2546		???	
	G3ZFJ	11:28	4	55	233	Windows 95:	Intel 80486
	K6MAR	11:40	4	2557	226	Windows 95:	Intel 80486
	K7GPS	10:49	2	2536	232	Windows 95:	Intel 80486
	K9AEG-1	10:49	2	860	228	Windows 95:	Intel 80486
	K9GD	11:57	10	804	233	Windows 95:	Intel Pentium
	KB1G	11:25	7	538	231	Windows 95:	Intel Pentium
	KB9GKG	11:27	10	711	232	Windows 95:	Intel Pentium
	KC6ETE	11:56	19	673	231	Windows 95:	Intel Pentium
	KC6ETE-5	11:41	12	673	231	Windows 95:	Intel Pentium
	KE0LY	11:23	3	962	231	Windows 95:	Intel Pentium
	KF4ERV-10	11:51	22	733	233	Windows NT:	Intel Pentium
	KN4HX	11:52	9	1149	226	Windows 95:	Intel Pentium
	N0LRF	11:41	8	1204	233	Windows 95:	Intel 80486
	N0SMS-1	10:49	2	1208	233	Windows 95:	Intel 80486
	N0VHB	11:57	16	1254	228	Windows 95:	Intel Pentium
	N5LFA	11:45	10	1018	233	Windows 95:	Intel Pentium
	N5YXO	11:50	12	1533		???	
	N8YCL	11:51	13	648	233	Windows 95:	Intel Pentium
	VE2CJT	11:26	4	284	232	Windows 95:	Intel Pentium
	VE4GN	10:49	2	1302	227	Windows 95:	Intel Pentium
	W0IBM	11:51	18	1028	227	Windows 95:	Intel 80486
	W7CCY	11:38	3	2403	233	Windows 95:	Intel Pentium

KE2VW-11>APRS,WIDE*,WIDE,WIDE:!4223.32NT07913.42W#PHG5160/WIDE-RELAY-TRACE DIGIPEATER

Figure 4-24—The Flagged Station List of* WinAPRS *delineates the flagged stations received by your station.

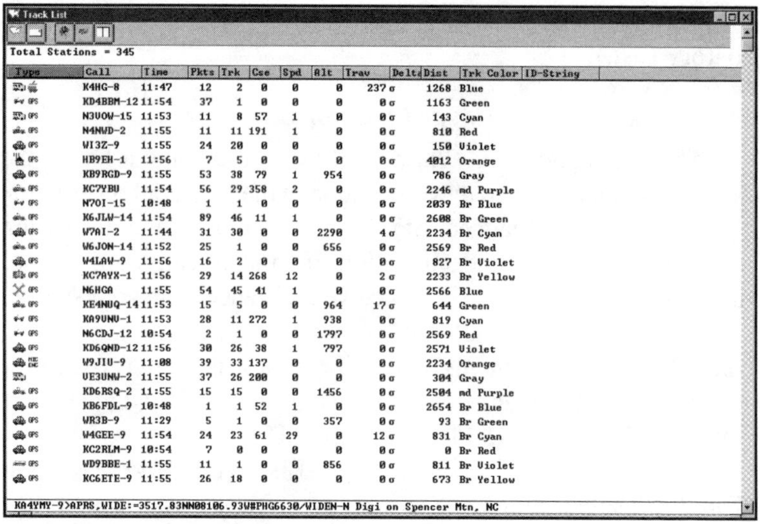

Track List

Total Stations = 345

Type	Call	Time	Pkts	Trk	Cse	Spd	Alt	Trav	Delta	Dist	Trk Color	ID-String
	K4HG-8	11:47	12	2	0	0	0	237	σ	1268	Blue	
GPS	KD4BBM-12	11:54	37	1	0	0	0	0	σ	1163	Green	
GPS	N3UOW-15	11:53	11	8	57	1	0	0	σ	143	Cyan	
GPS	N4NWD-2	11:55	11	11	191	1	0	0	σ	810	Red	
GPS	WI3Z-9	11:55	24	20	0	0	0	0	σ	150	Violet	
GPS	HB9EH-1	11:56	7	5	0	0	0	0	σ	4012	Orange	
GPS	KB9RGD-9	11:55	53	38	79	1	954	0	σ	786	Gray	
GPS	KC7YBU	11:54	56	29	358	2	0	0	σ	2246	md Purple	
GPS	N7OI-15	10:48	1	1	0	0	0	0	σ	2039	Br Blue	
GPS	K6JLW-14	11:54	89	46	11	1	0	0	σ	2608	Br Green	
GPS	W7AI-2	11:44	31	30	0	0	2290	4	σ	2234	Br Cyan	
GPS	W6JON-14	11:52	25	1	0	0	656	0	σ	2569	Br Red	
GPS	W4LAW-9	11:56	16	2	0	0	0	0	σ	827	Br Violet	
GPS	KC7AYX-1	11:56	29	14	268	12	0	2	σ	2233	Br Yellow	
GPS	N6HGA	11:55	54	45	41	1	0	0	σ	2566	Blue	
GPS	KE4NUQ-14	11:53	15	5	0	0	964	17	σ	644	Green	
GPS	KA9UNU-1	11:53	28	11	272	1	938	0	σ	819	Cyan	
GPS	N6CDJ-12	10:54	2	1	0	0	1797	0	σ	2569	Red	
GPS	KD6QND-12	11:56	30	26	38	1	797	0	σ	2571	Violet	
	W9JIU-9	11:08	39	33	137	0	0	0	σ	2234	Orange	
	VE3UNW-2	11:55	37	26	200	0	0	0	σ	304	Gray	
GPS	KD6RSQ-2	11:55	15	15	0	0	1456	0	σ	2504	md Purple	
GPS	KB6FDL-9	10:48	1	1	52	1	0	0	σ	2654	Br Blue	
GPS	WR3B-9	11:29	5	1	0	0	357	0	σ	93	Br Green	
GPS	W4GEE-9	11:54	24	23	61	29	0	12	σ	831	Br Cyan	
GPS	KC2RLM-9	10:54	7	0	0	0	0	0	σ	0	Br Red	
GPS	WD9BBE-1	11:55	11	1	0	0	856	0	σ	811	Br Violet	
GPS	KC6ETE-9	11:55	26	18	0	0	0	0	σ	673	Br Yellow	

KA4YMY-9>APRS,WIDE:=3517.83NN08106.93W#PHG6630/WIDEN-N Digi on Spencer Mtn, NC

Figure 4-25—The Tracked List of* WinAPRS *delineates the tracked stations received by your station.

Windows buttons, then click on the **OK** button.

Tracked Station List

Some versions of APRS permit you to view a list of stations that the software is tracking.

APRS+SA

To view the tracked station list in *APRS+SA*, click on the **Track** tab and refer to the Tracking List column.

MacAPRS

MacAPRS permits you to display a list of tracked stations received by your station in their order of receipt (the oldest first). The Track List includes the following information concerning each station: primary and secondary map icons, call sign, time of last packet received, number of packets received, number of packets received containing track data, course, speed, altitude, distance traveled, distance from your station, color of track, and contents of identification string, if any. (**Figure 4-25** illustrates the Tracked List of *WinAPRS*, which is very similar to the *MacAPRS* Tracked List.)

To view this information, select Track List from the Lists menu.

WinAPRS

WinAPRS permits you to display a list of tracked stations received by your station in their order of receipt (the oldest first). The Track List includes the following information concerning each station: primary and secondary map icons, call sign, time of last packet received, number of packets received, number of packets received containing track data, course, speed, altitude, distance traveled, distance from your station, color of track, and contents of identification string, if any. (Figure 4-25 illustrates the Tracked List of *WinAPRS*.)

To view this information, select Track List from the Lists menu.

Map List

Some versions of APRS permit you to display a list of the maps that are currently configured for use with the software.

APRS (DOS)

To view the map list with *APRS (DOS)*, press **M** (for Maps), then press **C** (for Configuration), and finally **L** (for List).

MacAPRS

In *MacAPRS*, select Map List from the Lists menu to view the list of maps.

pocketAPRS

With *pocketAPRS*, tap the MENU icon on the Palm III, then select Edit Map List from the Main menu. (To exit the Map List Maintenance window, tap the MENU icon and select another function.)

WinAPRS

In *WinAPRS*, select Map List from the Lists menu to view the list of maps.

Icon List

Some versions of APRS allow you to view all the icons that may be used to represent stations and objects on the map.

(**Figure 4-26** illustrates all the map icons available in APRS, their keyboard equivalents, and names.)

The following describes how to obtain the Icon List with each version of APRS.

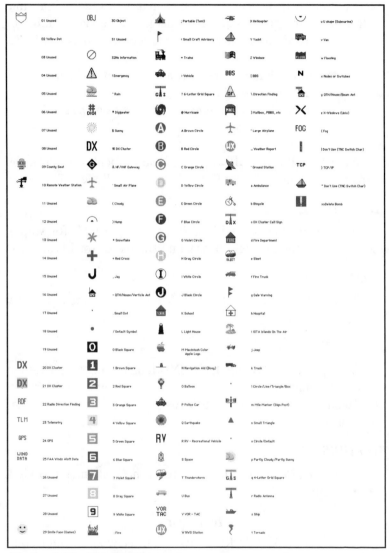

Figure 4-26—The APRS map icons.

APRS (DOS)

Press **F1**, then type **S** (for Symbols) to display the icons in their ASCII order.

APRS+SA

To view the icons in *APRS+SA*:
1. Click on the Setup menu, then click on the **Main Parameters** tab.
2. Click on the **Symbol** button to view the primary table of icons.
3. Click on the **Secondary Table** tab to view the secondary table of icons.
4. Click on the close box in the Transmitted Symbol and Setup windows when you are finished viewing the icons.

MacAPRS

Select Icon List from the Lists menu to display the following information concerning each icon: the icon itself, the alphanumeric characters that represent the icon, and the name of the icon.

TH-D7

To view the icons that the TH-D7 can display:
1. Press the **MENU** button, then press **2** and **5**.
2. Press the **up** or **down** buttons to scroll through the 15 icons that the TH-D7 can display.
3. When you are finished viewing the icons, press the **ESC** button three times.

WinAPRS

Select Icon List from the Lists menu to display the following information concerning each icon: the icon itself, the alphanumeric characters that represent the icon, and the name of the icon.

APRServers and IGates

Some APRS stations (called IGates) are connected to the Internet in order to relay the APRS data they receive locally to central Internet sites called APRServers. The APRServers massages this data (deleting bad and duplicate packets), then allows other stations to access that data in order to view APRS activity worldwide.

If the computer you use for running APRS is connected to the Internet, you can connect to an APRServer and display international APRS activity on your APRS maps. You may also access this data with a Java-capable Web browser by accessing an APRServer Internet site such as **http://www.aprs.net/usa1.html**.

By setting your APRS software to permit it to feed your local activity to the Internet, your station becomes an IGate. All this thanks to the programming skills of Steve Dimse, K4HG, who is responsible for the creation and implementation of the APRServer and IGate concepts.

In addition to giving you the capability to view worldwide APRS activity, IGates permit you to originate one-line email messages to legitimate Internet addresses. After properly addressing the message and transmitting it on the air, it is relayed to the Internet by any IGate that receives it (and is properly configured to relay it). After the relay, the IGate sends an acknowledgment over the air to the originating station.

To originate a message, simply address it to EMAIL and insert the Internet address as the first item in the message. For example, to send email to **n1ed@arrl.net**, you address the message to EMAIL and the contents of the message would look something like this:

n1ed@arrl.net Are you going to Dayton this year?

After transmitting the message, you will receive a message like "Email message delivered OK" from any IGate that handles it. Yes—this implies that more than one IGate will relay it to the Internet, but I think you will agree that is a small price to pay for this capability.

APRS (DOS)

To view APRServer data with *APRS (DOS)*, during setup, configure *APRS (DOS)* for connection to a modem rather than a TNC, then proceed as follows:

1. Press **F** (for Files), then **G** (for Get). This causes *APRS (DOS)* to download live backup files for each area of the country from the *APRS (DOS)* server.

2. After downloading, press **F** (for Files), then **L** (for Load) to load a downloaded file into *APRS (DOS)* in order to view the APRServer data.

APRS+SA

To receive APRS data from the APRServer with *APRS+SA* (and display the data on Street Atlas maps):

1. Click the Setup menu.
2. When the Setup window appears, click on the **Internet** tab.
3. When the **Internet** tab appears, configure its settings as desired. For example, click on the **Gate TNC** data stream to **Internet** button to relay your local APRS activity to the APRServer.
4. Click on the **Connect** button.
5. Select **Close** from the File menu.

MacAPRS

To receive APRS data from the APRServer with *MacAPRS*, select **TCP/IP Connections** from the Settings menu, then select **Conn to APRServe Network**.

To configure the settings regarding APRServer with *MacAPRS*:

1. Select TCP/IP Connections from the Settings menu, then select TCP server settings.
2. When the APRS TCP Server Settings window appears, select its options as desired. For example, click on the **Feed (Echo) local data to TCP/IP** button to relay your local APRS activity to the APRServer.
3. Click on the **OK** button.

WinAPRS

To receive APRS data from the APRServer with *WinAPRS*, select TCP/IP Connections from the Settings menu, then select **Connect to APRServe Network**.

To configure the settings regarding APRServer with *WinAPRS*:

1. Select TCP/IP Connections from the Settings menu, then select TCP server settings.
2. When the TCP Settings window appears, select its options as desired. For example, click on the **Feed (echo) local data to TCP/IP** button to relay your local APRS activity to the APRServer.
3. Click on the **OK** button.

APPENDIX A

TECHNICAL SUPPORT

Technical support for APRS is available via the Internet at a variety of Web sites and email lists. The following paragraphs list the sites and email lists devoted to the current releases of APRS software.

WEB SITES

The following sites provide a variety of information and technical support for the various flavors of APRS software.
- *APRS (DOS)* — **http://web.usna.navy.mil/~bruninga/ aprs.html**
- *APRS/CE* — email **aprsce@iwhereto.com**
- *APRS+SA* — **http://www.tapr.org/~kh2z/aprsplus/**
- *MacAPRS* — **http://aprs.rutgers.edu**
- *pocketAPRS* — **http://www.pocketaprs.com/**
- *WinAPRS* — **http://aprs.rutgers.edu**
- *XAPRS* — **http://aprs.rutgers.edu**
- *XASTIR* — **http://www.eazy.net/users/fgiannan/linux/**

EMAIL LISTS

Tucson Amateur Packet Radio (TAPR) sponsors the following email lists devoted to supporting APRS.
- *APRSSIG* is intended for the discussion of all APRS topics.
- *AO16APRS* is devoted to the discussion of using APRS with Amateur Radio satellites.
- *APRSFD* is intended for the discussion of using APRS in conjunction with Field Day operations.
- *APRSNEWS* distributes announcements concerning new releases of APRS software.

- *APRSSPEC* is intended for the discussion of the APRS protocol documentation project.
- *HTAPRS* is devoted to the discussion of APRS topics related to the Kenwood TH-D7 handheld transceiver.
- *MIC-E* is intended for the discussion of the MIC-E module.
- *PROPNET* is devoted to an ongoing VHF propagation experiment using APRS.

To subscribe to any of these lists, go to
http://www.tapr.org/cgi-bin/lyris.pl?site=tapr

APPENDIX B

COMMANDS

The following tables list and briefly describe all the commands in the five versions of APRS software and the Kenwood TH-D7 transceiver APRS mode.

APRS (DOS)

You choose most *APRS (DOS)* commands by typing the uppercase characters of the command name. For example, to select the Positions command, you type the letter P; to select the Controls > Filters > dX command, you type C, then F, then X. A few *APRS (DOS)* commands are selected by typing a number (e.g., 9), pressing a control-character (e.g., [Home]), or pressing a function-key (e.g., [F5]).

Some *APRS (DOS)* commands use the control character [Alt-S]. To enter this control character, hold down the Control [Alt] key and press the S key.

Keyboard Command	Description [default, if any]
[	display more map labels
[Alt-S] > Df > dfJr	turn on/off DFjr mode [off]
[Alt-S] > Df > Dfsp	turn on/off DFSP mode [off]
[Alt-S] > Df > Magnetic_variation	turn on/off for magnetic DF bearings and headings [off]
[Alt-S] > Formats > Compressed	turn on/off packet compression mode [off]
[Alt-S] > Formats > Grid_in_to	turn on/off grid-in-to mode [off]
[Alt-S] > Formats > Meteor_scatter	turn on/off meteor scatter mode [off]
[Alt-S] > Formats > Normal	turn on/off normal APRS operation [on]
[Alt-S] > Formats > Space	turn on/off spacecraft mode [off]
[Alt-S] > Gps > Dgps	select Differential GPS mode
[Alt-S] > Gps > Modes > Arnav	select ARNAV GPS mode
[Alt-S] > Gps > Modes > Both_gga/rmc	select both the GGA and RMC sentence format GPS modes
[Alt-S] > Gps > Modes > Esp	select E^ Single Port (ESP) GPS mode
[Alt-S] > Gps > Modes > Gga	select GGA sentence format GPS mode
[Alt-S] > Gps > Modes > Hsp	select GPS Hardware Single Port mode
[Alt-S] > Gps > Modes > Klynas	configure APRS (DOS) to use Klynas Engineering's Streets-On-Disk
[Alt-S] > Gps > Modes > My$	select MY$ GPS mode
[Alt-S] > Gps > Modes > NMEA_log	turn on/off saving NMEA data to a file [off]
[Alt-S] > Gps > Modes > Rmc	select the RMC sentence format GPS mode
[Alt-S] > Gps > Modes > Spm	select GPS Single Port Mode
[Alt-S] > Gps > Off/on_gps	disable SPM or HSP
[Alt-S] > Gps > Plot	display plot of GPS satellites and their signal strengths
[Alt-S] > Gps > Time_sync	set system clock from local NMEA/GPS equipment
[Alt-S] > Gps > Waypoints	send waypoints to GPS

[Alt-S] > Modes > alt_Net	turn on/off special function net mode [off]
[Alt-S] > Modes > Auto_space	turn on/off automatic spacecraft mode [off]
[Alt-S] > Modes > Master	configure computer as the master in a Zip LAN
[Alt-S] > Modes > Out_new_gga	output GGA-formatted position packet upon receipt of new position
[Alt-S] > Modes > Special	turn on/off special event mode [off]
[Alt-S] > Modes > Zip_lan	configure the computer for a LAN where multiple computers share one TNC
[Alt-S] > Other > Above_avg_terrain	enter the height above average terrain (HAAT) of your station
[Alt-S] > Other > Beeps	turn on/off APRS sound [on]
[Alt-S] > Other > Dst	turn on/off Daylight Saving Time clock setting
[Alt-S] > Other > Ega	turn on/off EGA monitor operation [off]
[Alt-S] > Other > Game	play chess with APRS (DOS)
[Alt-S] > Other > Lock	lock computer keyboard
[Alt-S] > Other > Midnight_save	save all APRS (DOS) files at midnight
[Alt-S] > Other > Redraw	select rate of screen redraw
[Alt-S] > Other > Screen_saver	enables/disables screen saver function [off]
[Alt-S] > Other > Zone	change time zone of your station
[Alt-S] > Ports > Dual_ports	configure software for connection to dual-port TNC
[Alt-S] > Ports > Modem_remote	configure software for connection to a telephone-line modem
[Alt-S] > Ports > Single_port	configure software for connection to single-port TNC
[Alt-S] > Rates	select display and sending rates for GPS, weather and direction finding data
[Alt-S] > Save	save current map and configuration
[Alt-S] > Tnc	configure TNC with TNC APRS parameters

[Alt-T]	display received telemetry data
[Delete]	deselect (unhook) an object
[Down Arrow]	move cursor down
[End]	center map on the default location of your station
[Enter]	select (hook) an object
[Escape]	move cursor to center of map
[F1]	display APRS (DOS) help
[F10]	turn on/off Windows mode [off]
[F2]	compose and transmit reply to last received message
[F3]	display more map labels
[F4]	display fewer map labels
[F5]	enter fade point for omni-directional direction finding
[F6]	configure the speed of your mobile station to 0
[F7]	select low (23-line) or high (43-line) resolution display [low]
[F8]	plot an immediate fix in GPS/HSP mode
[F9]	adjust map size to display all stations
[Home]	center map at current cursor position
[Insert]	move selected (hooked) object
[Left Arrow]	move cursor left
[Page Down]	magnify map
[Page Up]	reduce map magnification
[Right Arrow]	move cursor right
[Space Bar]	display/redraw currently selected map
[Tab]	display status of Control and Setup command parameters

[Up Arrow]	move cursor up
]	display fewer map labels
1	display default map
3	display map saved for key 3
5	display map saved for key 5
7	display map saved for key 7
9	display map saved for key 9
All	display all received messages and beacons in chronological order
Bulletins	display last 22 received bulletins
Controls > Bands > 2_port	configure APRS (DOS) for dual-port TNC operation
Controls > Bands > Hf	configure APRS (DOS) for HF TNC operation
Controls > Bands > Vhf	configure APRS (DOS) for VHF/UHF TNC operation
Controls > Cw > Disable	disables sounding received beacons in CW
Controls > Cw > Enable	enables sounding received beacons in CW [off]
Controls > Cw > Set_speed	select words-per-minute of CW soundings [15]
Controls > Cw > Test	test CW sounding function
Controls > Dr	turn on/off dead reckoning [off]
Controls > Filters > Fade	turn on/off filtering currently inactive stations [on]
Controls > Filters > Hf_gateway	turn on/off filtering of stations gatewayed from HF [off]
Controls > Filters > Junk	turn on/off filtering data embedded with control characters [off]
Controls > Filters > Limit	turn on/off filtering of long Unprotocol paths [off]
Controls > Filters > Other_beacons	turn on/off filtering non-beacon packets [on]
Controls > Filters > Pos_filter	turn on/off filtering of random GPS data errors [on]
Controls > Log	turn on/off automatic logging of track histories [off]
Controls > Metric	select map measurements in kilometers or miles [miles]

Command	Description
Controls > Uplinks	turn on/off transmitting your object data [on]
Controls > Xmt	turn on/off normal transmitting [off]
Digis	display digipeaters used by all received stations
Erase	delete outgoing message
Files > Append	load a backup file without losing current station data
Files > Dos	transfer to DOS
Files > Ethernet	periodically save Backup file to storage device on Ethernet LAN
Files > Get	connect via telephone line modem to receive worldwide APRS activity
Files > Hang-up	hang-up phone manually when connected to a modem
Files > Load	load a backup file
Files > New	create a new file
Files > Print	print selected file
Files > Replay	load and play saved track history files
Files > Save	save current data
Files > sOrt	sort station list in chronological order with oldest stations first
Goto	move cursor to your station or tracked station
Heard	display packets per hour received from each station during previous 24 hours
Inputs > Add_object	add an object to the APRS map at the current cursor position
Inputs > Df	enter a beam heading or signal report for direction finding
Inputs > My > Bulletin_group	enter the bulletin group for your station
Inputs > My > Heading	enter the direction of your vehicle
Inputs > My > Message_group	enter the message group for your station

Command	Description
Inputs > My > Posit	enter the position of your station
Inputs > My > Radar	configure proximity sensor for your station
Inputs > My > Status	enter the status text for your station
Inputs > Pwr_ht_gain	enter the transmitter power and antenna parameters of your station
Inputs > Resources	enter resource information
Inputs > Save_pos	save the current position of your station as an object
Inputs > Up_pos	save the current position of your station as an object
Just > All	clear map and display all stations
Just > Digipeaters	clear map and display only digipeaters
Just > Icons	clear map and display only station icons
Just > Mobiles	clear map and display only moving stations
Just > Non_qth	clear map and display all stations that are not QTHs
Just > oBjects	clear map and display only objects
Just > One	clear map and display only one station type
Just > Print	print a selected subset of objects to the printer
Just > Special	clear map and display only stations using special symbols
Just > Wx	clear map and display only weather stations
Kill	delete incoming message
List > Dx	display list of latest received DX spots
List > Log	display list of latest received status, message, and telemetry packets
List > Resources	display list of other local APRS assets
List > Status	display list of latest received status packets
List > Telemetry	display list of latest received telemetry packets
Maps > Config > Background	change map background color
Maps > Config > Change_map_list	change current MAPLIST.XXX file

Maps > Config > List_map_list	display list of all available MAPLIST.XXX files
Maps > Config > Offset_datum	offset map to match known GPS position
Maps > Distros	display list of all loaded maps
Maps > Down	magnify map
Maps > Features > *railroad	turn on/off display of railroads on map [on]
Maps > Features > All	turn on/off display of all map features [on]
Maps > Features > Borders	turn on/off display of map borders [on]
Maps > Features > Calls	turn on/off display of call signs on map [on]
Maps > Features > Dim	turn on/off dimmed map display [off]
Maps > Features > Headings	turn on/off display of headings on map [on]
Maps > Features > Labels	turn on/off display of labels on map [on]
Maps > Features > Roads	turn on/off display of roads on map [on]
Maps > Features > Water	turn on/off display of waterways on map [on]
Maps > Hierarchy	display hierarchy of available maps
Maps > Lock	lock currently displayed map to override automatic map selection function
Maps > Mile_markers	locate mile marker on a U.S. Interstate highway (except California)
Maps > Overlays > Atv	display Amateur Television (ATV) overlay on map
Maps > Overlays > Crash	display crash overlay on map
Maps > Overlays > Digipeaters	display digipeater overlay on map
Maps > Overlays > Frequencies	display APRS frequency overlay on map
Maps > Overlays > Gates	display gateway overlay on map
Maps > Overlays > National_weather_service	display NWS station overlay on map

Command	Description
Maps > Overlays > Other	display other overlays on map
Maps > Overlays > Radio Shack	display Radio Shack overlay on map
Maps > Overlays > Stores	display ham radio store overlay on map
Maps > Overlays > Zips	display ZIP Code overlay on map
Maps > Plots > Borders	display perimeters of all selectable maps
Maps > Plots > Cap_grids	overlay Civil Air Patrol (CAP) grid squares on map
Maps > Plots > compressed_Format	display compressed formats in ASCII
Maps > Plots > Df	display coverage circles representing reported signal strengths of unknown source
Maps > Plots > Grid_square	overlay 2-character Maidenhead grid squares on map
Maps > Plots > Pwr_ht_gain	display circles representing station coverage area
Maps > Plots > Range_rings	display coverage circles at 1, 3/4, 1/2, and 1/4 of the coverage circle scale
Maps > Plots > Traffic	displays lines between stations exchanging messages
Maps > Save	save current map
Maps > Show > Alt	display map, if any, under currently displayed map
Maps > Show > Callsigns	display call signs
Maps > Show > Map_overlays	display map overlays
Maps > Up	reduce map
Next	move cursor to next weather station and display its weather data
Operations > Alarms_clear	clear your alarms
Operations > Communications	disable APRS and open window for direct communications with device connected to serial port
Operations > Digipath	configure alternative Unprotocol paths

Operations > Find	locate a call sign or grid square
Operations > Replay_tracks	play a track history
Operations > Unprotocol	configure your primary Unprotocol path
Positions	display received APRS position packets
Quit	quit APRS (DOS)
Read	display transmitted and received messages
Send	compose and transmit message or bulletin
Traffic	display last 23 lines of received traffic
Unproto	configure the normal digipeater path for your station
View	display scrolling list of all received packets
Weather > Alarms > Clear_alarm	clear weather alarms
Weather > Alarms > High_temp	configure high temperature alarm
Weather > Alarms > Low_temp	configure low temperature alarm
Weather > Alarms > Rain	configure rain alarm
Weather > Alarms > rAnge	limit weather alarms from stations within a selectable distance
Weather > Alarms > Wind	configure wind alarm
Weather > Alarms > Zero_rain	set the rain gauge measurement to 0
Weather > Callsign_format > Baro	display atmospheric pressure and time of report
Weather > Callsign_format > Callsigns	display call signs of weather stations
Weather > Callsign_format > None	clear weather data display
Weather > Callsign_format > Other_symbols	turn on/off alternate weather symbols [off]
Weather > Callsign_format > Spd/alt	display wind speed
Weather > Callsign_format > Temps	display temperature and rainfall reading
Weather > Callsign_format > Winds	display wind speed and rainfall readings and time of report

Command	Description
Weather > Displays > Just_wx	limit map display to weather stations
Weather > Displays > No_counties	do not display county weather alarms
Weather > Displays > Show_counties	display county weather alarms
Weather > Displays > Temps	display temperature data
Weather > Displays > Winds	display wind data
Weather > Enter	manually input a weather report
Weather > Log	saves received weather data in the track history file
Weather > Metric	use metric system for weather station data
Weather > Query	transmit an APRS weather station query packet
Xmt > All	transmit all your outstanding packets
Xmt > Bulletins	transmit all your outstanding bulletin packets
Xmt > Cq	transmit a CQ packet
Xmt > Last_ack	transmit a message acknowledgment
Xmt > Messages	transmit all your outstanding message packets
Xmt > Objects	transmit all your outstanding objects packets
Xmt > Posits	transmit all your outstanding position packets
Xmt > Query	transmit an APRS query packet
Xmt > Resource	transmit a resource information packet
Xmt > Status	transmit all your outstanding status packets
Yaxis	turn on/off 3-dimensional display of currently selected map [off]

APRS+SA

You choose most APRS+SA commands by selecting a command from a pull-down menu or pull-down sub-menu, for example, to enter the File > Start Logging TNC Data command, pull down the File menu and select Start Logging TNC Data. A few APRS+SA commands are selected by typing a control-character (e.g., [Home]).

When you open a tab in APRS+SA, you select commands for that tab from a pop-up menu. To view the pop-up menu, move the mouse cursor over the applicable tab window and press the right mouse button. (The commands for each tab are listed after the APRS+SA menu commands.)

Some APRS+SA commands have keyboard shortcuts, which are listed in brackets (e.g., [Ctrl-C]) in the Menu Command column. You enter these shortcuts by holding down the Control [Ctrl] key and pressing a second key, for example, to use the [Ctrl-C] shortcut, you press the C key, while holding down the Ctrl key.

Menu Command [Keyboard Shortcut]	Description
File > Open SA4/SA5/MN3 Overlay file	display Street Atlas overlay file on map
File > Clear Overlay file	remove Street Atlas overlay file from map
File > POS File to Map	display data from position log file on map
File > Open Position Log File	start saving position data to a file
File > Start Logging TNC Data	start saving TNC data to a file
File > Start Logging Internet Data	start saving Internet data to a file
File > Open Text Log File	load log file saved in text format
File > APRS+Text Editor	open text editor
File > Load Patch Files	load APRS+SA software patches
File > Exit	quit APRS+SA
Edit > Cut [Ctrl-X]	delete selected item and duplicate to clipboard
Edit > Copy [Ctrl-C]	duplicate selected item to clipboard

Command	Description
Edit > Paste [Ctrl-V]	insert item contained in clipboard
Edit > Find	locate item
Edit > Popup	display popup menu
View > Status Bar	turn on/off display of status bar
View > Tooltips	turn on/off display of tooltips
Setup	displays Setup window
Log	displays Event Log
Send > Send Message [Ctrl-M]	compose and transmit a message
Send > Transmit Position [Ctrl-P]	send position packet
Send > Transmit Station [Ctrl-S]	send status packet
Send > Send Bulletin [Ctrl-B]	compose and transmit a bulletin
Send > Send Weather Report [Ctrl-W]	compose and transmit a weather message
Send > Send Tactical Callsign	transmit tactical call sign
Object > Create Object from Map	create object located at lower left corner of map
Object > Create Object Manually	create object
Object > Create Object at My Current Location	create object located at current location of your station
Commands > Scrolling On/Off [Ctrl-Shift-P]	turn on/off map scrolling
Commands > Unproto Paths [Ctrl-Shift-U]	configure Unprotocol path(s) for your station
Commands > Map Features [Ctrl-Shift-M]	select map display options
Commands > Start Street Atlas [Ctrl-Shift-A]	begin running Street Atlas
Commands > Coordinate Convention [Ctrl-Shift-C]	display Coordinate Conversion window
Commands > TNC Commands > TNC Port 1 [Ctrl-Shift-1]	select TNC on serial port 1
Commands > TNC Commands > TNC Port 2 [Ctrl-Shift-2]	select TNC on serial port 2
Commands > TNC Commands > Send [Ctrl-C To TNC [Ctrl-C]	transmit control character Ctrl-C to TNC

Commands > TNC Commands > Send Three [Ctrl-Cs To TNC [Ctrl-R]	transmit three control character Ctrl-Cs to TNC
Commands > TNC Commands > Pico Position Text [Ctrl-E]	transmit position packet to PacComm Pico TNC
Commands > TNC Commands > Garmin Handheld Receivers	display Garmin GRMN/GRMN Interface window
Commands > TNC Commands > Tripmate > ASTRAL To TNC Port	use TNC port for Tripmate GPS communications
Commands > TNC Commands > Tripmate > ASTRAL To GPS Port	use GPS port for Tripmate GPS communications
Commands > TNC Commands > Flow Control Debugging - HSP	display Flow Control Debug window
Commands > ?APRS? [Ctrl-Q]	send APRS query packet
Commands > Time Filter > Off	process all data despite its age
Commands > Time Filter > 0.5, 1, 2, 3, 4, 8, 12, 24 Hours	ignore data older than selected time period
Commands > Range Filter > Off	process data from all stations despite their distance from your station
Commands > Range Filter > 3, 5, 10, 20, 40, 80, 160, 320, 640, 1280, 2560 Miles	ignore data from stations beyond selected distance from your station
Commands > Maps > Map Drawing On [Ctrl+=]	turn on map drawing
Commands > Maps > Map Drawing Off [Ctrl+-]	turn off map drawing
Commands > Maps > Locate Yourself On The Map [Ctrl-L]	display position of your station on map
Commands > Maps > Draw Map 1 through 9 [Ctrl-1 through Ctrl-9]	display selected map
Commands > Maps > Draw Next Map 0 [Ctrl-0]	display next map in Map tab list
Commands > Summary Window	display Summary window
Commands > Calculator [Ctrl-Alt-Shift-A]	display calculator

Command	Description
Commands > Clear > Clear All	remove contents of all windows
Commands > Clear > Clear Position Data	remove position data from all windows
Commands > Clear > Keep Most Recent	remove contents of all windows except the most recent data
Commands > Clear > Keep Station Within Range	remove contents of all windows except data related to stations within range of your station
Commands > Clear > Remove Lat/Long 0 90 180	remove data related to stations with latitudes or longitudes of 0, 90, and 180 degrees
Commands > Clear > Clear TNC Window	remove contents of TNC window
Commands > Clear > Clear TCP/IP Window	remove contents of TCP/IP window
Commands > Clear > Clear GPS Window	remove contents of GPS window
Commands > Speak Last Status Text [Ctrl-Shift-T]	convert text in last received status packet to speech
Commands > Internet Connect	connect to APRServer
Commands > Callsign Lookup on the Internet	connect to call sign server via the Internet
Speech > Enable	turn on text-to-speech function
Speech > Disable	turn off text-to-speech function
Speech > Stop	turn off text-to-speech function
Speech > Sound Effects On	enable sound effects
Speech > Sound Effects Off	disable sound effects
Bitmap	display map of North America
About	display information concerning APRS+SA
Positions Tab Popup Menu	Description
Locate > Current Position	display location of selected station on map
Locate > Stations in Range	display location (on map) of stations within range of selected station

Command	Description
Locate > Nearest Station To	display location (on map) of station nearest to selected station
Lists > Add to Keep Recent Only List	append selected station to Keep Recent Only List
Lists > Add to Ignore List	append selected station to Ignore List
Coordinates	copy coordinates of selected station in Coordinate Conversion window
Keep Most Recent Position Only	retain only the newest position data of selected station
Delete Station	remove selected station
Archive Position Data to Disk	save position data of selected station to disk
Add to Tracking List	add selected station to Tracking List
Show in History Tab	display selected station to History tab list
Make Location Map Center	redraw map centered on location of selected station
Filter Location Data	remove location of selected station from map
Send Message To	compose and transmit message to selected station
Upload to Garmin GPS	transfer position data of selected station to Garmin GPS receiver
Clear Selection	deselect selected station
Range to Station	display distance to selected station from your station
?APRS?	send APRS query packet to selected station
Sort by Range	display stations in list arranged according to distance from your station
View > Report Mode	display station data as a report
View > List Mode	display station data as a list
View > Adjust Column Width	change the width of the displayed columns for best viewing
Print	print window contents
Clipboard > Copy Rows to Clipboad	duplicate selected rows to clipboard
Clipboard > Copy Callsign to Clipboard	duplicate call sign field of selected row to clipboard
Clipboard > Copy Text to Clipboard	duplicate text field of selected row to clipboard

Track Tab Popup Menu

	Description
Locate > Current Position	display location of selected station on map
Locate > Stations in Range	display location (on map) of stations within range of selected station
Locate > Nearest Station To	display location (on map) of station nearest to selected station
Lists > Add to Keep Recent Only List	append selected station to Keep Recent Only List
Lists > Add to Ignore List	append selected station to Ignore List
Coordinates	copy coordinates of selected station in Coordinate Conversion window
Keep Most Recent Position Only	retain only the newest position data of selected station
Delete Station	remove selected station
Archive Position Data to Disk	save position data of selected station to disk
Add to Tracking List	add selected station to Tracking List
Show in History Tab	display selected station to History tab list
Make Location Map Center	redraw map centered on location of selected station
Filter Location Data	remove location of selected station from map
Send Message To	compose and transmit message to selected station
Upload to Garmin GPS	transfer position data of selected station to Garmin GPS receiver
Clear Selection	deselect selected station
Range to Station	display distance to selected station from your station
?APRS?	send APRS query packet to selected station
Sort by Range	display stations in list arranged according to distance from your station
View > Report Mode	display station data as a report
View > List Mode	display station data as a list
View > Adjust Column Width	change the width of the displayed columns for best viewing

Print	print window contents
Clipboard > Copy Rows to Clipboard	duplicate selected rows to clipboard
Clipboard > Copy Callsign to Clipboard	duplicate call sign field of selected row to clipboard
Clipboard > Copy Text to Clipboard	duplicate selected text to clipboard

History Tab Popup Menu

	Description
Locate Position	display location of selected station on map
Locate Stations in Range	display location (on map) of stations within range of selected station
Locate Nearest Station To	display location (on map) of station nearest to selected station
Range	display distance and compass direction to selected station
Coordinates	copy coordinates of selected station in Coordinate Conversion window
Delete Position Fix	remove selected position packet from window
Send Message To	compose and transmit message to selected station
Upload to Garmin GPS	transfer position data of selected station to Garmin GPS receiver
Add to Tracking List	add selected station to Tracking List
Lists > Add to Keep Recent Only List	append selected station to Keep Recent Only List
Lists > Add to Ignore List	append selected station to Ignore List
Filter Position Reports	remove position packets according to packet filtering criteria
Adjust Column Width	change the width of the displayed columns for best viewing
Print	print window contents
Copy Rows to Clipboard	duplicate selected rows to clipboard

Maps Tab Popup Menu

	Description
Clear List	remove contents of list

Command	Description
Delete	remove selected item from list
Maps > Map 1: Map 1 through Map 9: Map 9	add Map 1: Map 1 through Map 9: Map 9 to list
Weather > Temperature	add Temperature to list
Weather > Baro. Pressure	add Baro. Pressure to list
Weather > Wind Speed	add Wind Speed to list
Weather > Wind Direction	add Wind Direction to list
Weather > Winds	add Winds to list
Weather > Humidity	add Humidity to list
Maps by Icon > Digipeaters	add Digipeaters to list
Maps by Icon > By Icon 1 through By Icon 4	add By Icon 1 through By Icon 4 to list
Other Maps > History Page Map	add History Page to list
Other Maps > Posit Text Search	add Posit Text to list
Other Maps > Status Text Search	add Status Text to list
Other Maps > Fixed Stations	add Fixed Stations to list
Other Maps > Moving Stations	add Moving Stations to list
Other Maps > HF Gated Stations	add HF Gated Stations to list
Other Maps > APRS+SA Stations	add APRS+SA Stations to list
Custom Scripted > Create Custom Script	create custom map
Custom Scripted > (list of custom maps)	add custom map to list

Status Tab Popup Menu

	Description
Delete Message(s)	
Send Message To	compose and transmit message to selected station
Clear Page	remove contents of window

Locate on Map	display location of selected station on map
Locate Stations in Range	display location (on map) of stations within range of selected station
Locate Nearest Station To	display location (on map) of station nearest to selected station
Range to Station	display distance to selected station from your station
Sort by Range	display stations in list arranged according to distance from your station
Sort by Icon	display stations in list arranged according to icon
Show History	display all the packets received from selected station
Adjust Column Width	change the width of the displayed columns for best viewing
Print	print window contents
Clipboard > Copy to Clipboad	duplicate selected item to clipboard
Clipboard > Copy Text to Clipboard	duplicate text field of selected row to clipboard
Clipboard > Copy Callsign to Clipboard	duplicate call sign field of selected row to clipboard

Traffic Tab Popup Menu

Description

Delete Message(s)	remove selected message(s)
Delete Messages From/To	remove messages from/to station originating selected message
Send Message To	compose and transmit message to station originating selected message
Clear Page	remove contents of window
Locate on Map	display location of station originating selected message
Locate Stations in Range	display location (on map) of stations within range of station originating selected message
Locate Nearest Station To	display location (on map) of station nearest to station originating selected message
Show History	display all the packets received from station originating selected message

Range to Station	display distance between your station and the station originating selected message
Range Between Stations	display distance between originating and receiving station of selected message
Remove Ack's	delete acknowledgement packets from history of listed stations
Adjust Column Width	change the width of the displayed columns for best viewing
Print	print window contents
Clipboard > Copy to Clipboard	duplicate selected item to clipboard
Clipboard > Copy Text to Clipboard	duplicate text of selected message to clipboard
Clipboard > Copy From Callsign to Clipboard	duplicate call sign of station originating selected message to clipboard
Clipboard > Copy To Callsign to Clipboard	duplicate call sign of station receiving selected message to clipboard

Messages Tab Popup Menu
(Window for Messages To/From Your Station)

	Description
Delete	remove selected message
Delete Ack'ed	remove acknowledged messages
Reset Interval	change interval field to 7.5
Transmit Now	send selected message immediately
Copy Message	duplicate contents of selected message in message composition window
Clear Page	remove contents of window
Clear Bulletins	remove bulletins from window
Clear Messages	remove messages from window
Path > I = Internet TCP/IP Port TCP	send message via Internet
Path > 1 = RELAY,WIDE Port 1	send message via Unprotocol path 1

Path > 2 = RELAY,WIDE Port 1	send message via Unprotocol path 1
Path > 3 = RELAY,WIDE Port 1	send message via Unprotocol path 1
Path > 4 = RELAY,WIDE Port 1	send message via Unprotocol path 1
Path > N = RELAY,WIDE Port 1	send message via Unprotocol path N
Path > S = RELAY,WIDE Port 1	send message via Unprotocol path S
Path > E = RELAY,WIDE Port 1	send message via Unprotocol path E
Path > W = RELAY,WIDE Port 1	send message via Unprotocol path W
Path > ECHO = ECHO Port 1	send message via Unprotocol path ECHO
Path > EG = ECHO,GATE Port 1	send message via Unprotocol path EG
Path > WIDE = WIDE Port 1	send message via Unprotocol path WIDE
Path > WW = WIDE,WIDE Port 1	send message via Unprotocol path WW
Path > = Default	send message via default Unprotocol path
Stop Transmission	cease sending selected message
Suspend Transmission	postpone sending selected message
Resume Transmission	continue sending selected message
Manual Acknowledge	set selected message manually
Adjust Column Width	change the width of the displayed columns for best viewing
Clipboard > Copy Text and Run	duplicate text of selected message to clipboard
Clipboard > Copy Callsign to Clipboard	duplicate call sign of station receiving selected message to clipboard
Clipboard > Copy Text to Clipboard	duplicate text of selected message to clipboard

Messages Tab Popup Menu
(Window for All Messages)

	Description
Delete Message(s)	remove selected message(s)
Send Message To	compose and transmit message to station originating selected message
Time Entered	display time selected message was entered
Copy Message	duplicate contents of selected message in message composition window
Sort by Callsign/Message Number	arrange messages in window by call sign and message number
Clear Page	remove contents of window
Locate on Map	display location (on map) of station originating selected message
Locate Stations in Range	display location (on map) of stations within range of station originating selected message
Locate Nearest Station To	display location (on map) of station nearest to station originating selected message
Range to Station	display distance from your station to station originating selected message
Show History	display all the packets received from station originating selected message
Adjust Column Width	change the width of the displayed columns for best viewing
Print	print window contents
Clipboard > Copy Text and Run	duplicate text of selected message to clipboard
Clipboard > Copy to Clipboard	duplicate selected item to clipboard
Clipboard > Copy Text to Clipboard	duplicate text of selected message to clipboard
Clipboard > Copy Callsign to Clipboard	duplicate call sign of station originating selected message to clipboard

Bulletins Tab Popup Menu

	Description
Delete Message(s)	remove selected bulletin(s)
Delete Messages From/To	remove bulletins from/to station originating selected bulletin
Send Message To	compose and transmit message to station originating selected bulletin
Time Entered	display time selected bulletin was entered
Clear Page	remove contents of window
Locate on Map	display location (on map) of station originating selected bulletin
Locate Stations in Range	display location (on map) of stations within range of station originating selected bulletin
Locate Nearest Station To	display location (on map) of station nearest to station originating selected bulletin
Adjust Column Width	change the width of the displayed columns for best viewing
Print	print window contents
Clipboard > Copy Text and Run	duplicate text of selected message to clipboard
Clipboard > Copy to Clipboad	duplicate selected item to clipboard
Clipboard > Copy Text to Clipboard	duplicate text of selected bulletin to clipboard
Clipboard > Copy To Callsign to Clipboard	duplicate call sign of station originating selected bulletin to clipboard

Objects Tab Popup Menu
(Window for Your Station's Objects)

	Description
Transmit Now	send selected object packet immediately
State > Active	resume sending packets for selected object
State > Kill	cease sending packets for selected object
State > Inactive	suspend sending packets for selected object
State > Persistent	set state of selected object to persistent

Command	Description
Transmit Interval > Every 5, 10, 15, 20, 30, 60 Minutes, 2, 3, 4, 6, 12 Hours	select how often packets for selected object are sent
Edit Object	change characteristics of selected object
Delete Object(s)	remove selected object
Create Object > Create Object from Map	create object located at lower left corner of map
Create Object > Create Object Manually	create object
Create Object > Create Object at My Current Location	create object located at current location of your station
Read SA Object File	load Street Atlas object file into APRS+SA
Clear Page	remove contents of window
Locate on Map	display location of selected object on map
Locate Stations in Range	display location (on map) of stations within range of selected object
Locate Nearest Station To	display location (on map) nearest station to selected object
Range to Object	display distance to selected object from your station
Adjust Column Width	change the width of the displayed columns for best viewing
Print	print window contents
Copy to Clipboad	duplicate selected item to clipboard

Objects Tab Popup Menu
(Window for All Objects)

	Description
Locate > Current Position	display location of selected object on map
Locate > Stations in Range	display location (on map) of stations within range of selected object
Locate > Nearest Station To	display location (on map) of station nearest to selected object
Lists > Add to Keep Recent Only List	append selected object to Keep Recent Only List

Lists > Add to Ignore List	append selected object to Ignore List
Coordinates	copy coordinates of selected object in Coordinate Conversion window
Keep Most Recent Position Only	retain only the newest position data of selected object
Delete Station	remove selected object
Archive Position Data to Disk	save position data of selected object to disk
Add to Tracking List	add selected object to Tracking List
Show in History Tab	display selected object to History tab list
Make Location Map Center	redraw map centered on location of selected object
Filter Location Data	remove location of selected object from map
Send Message To	compose and transmit message to station originating selected object
Upload to Garmin GPS	transfer position data of selected object to Garmin GPS receiver
Clear Selection	deselect selected object
Range to Station	display distance to selected object from your station
?APRS?	send APRS query packet to selected object
Sort by Range	display objects in list arranged according to distance from your station
View > Report Mode	display objects data as a report
View > List Mode	display objects data as a list
View > Adjust Column Width	change the width of the displayed columns for best viewing
Print	print window contents
Clipboard > Copy Rows to Clipboard	duplicate selected rows to clipboard
Clipboard > Copy Callsign to Clipboard	duplicate call sign field of selected row to clipboard
Clipboard > Copy Text to Clipboard	duplicate text field of selected row to clipboard

Weather Tab Popup Menu

	Description
Delete Message(s)	remove selected message(s)
Send Message To	compose and transmit message to selected station
Clear Page	remove contents of window
Map > Temperature	display temperature of selected message at station location on map
Map > Barometric Pressure	display barometric pressure of selected message at station location on map
Map > Winds	display wind speed of selected message at station location on map
Locate on Map	display location of selected station on map
Locate Stations in Range	display location (on map) of stations within range of selected station
Locate Nearest Station To	display location (on map) of station nearest to selected station
Range to Station	display distance to selected station from your station
Sort by Range	display stations in list arranged according to distance from your station
Show History	display all the packets received from selected station
Adjust Column Width	change the width of the displayed columns for best viewing
Print	print window contents
Copy to Clipboad	duplicate selected item to clipboard

Telemetry Tab Popup Menu

	Description
Delete Observation(s)	remove selected telemetry
Send Message To	compose and transmit message to selected station
Clear Page	remove contents of window
Adjust Column Width	change the width of the displayed columns for best viewing
Print	print window contents
Copy to Clipboad	duplicate selected item to clipboard

TNC Tab Popup Menu

	Description
Undo	cancel previous action
Cut	delete selected item and duplicate to clipboard
Copy	duplicate selected item to clipboard
Paste	insert item contained in clipboard
Delete	remove selected item
Select All	choose all items

GPS Tab Popup Menu

	Description
Undo	cancel previous action
Cut	delete selected item and duplicate to clipboard
Copy	duplicate selected item to clipboard
Paste	insert item contained in clipboard
Delete	remove selected item
Select All	choose all items

TCP Tab Popup Menu

	Description
Undo	cancel previous action
Cut	delete selected item and duplicate to clipboard
Copy	duplicate selected item to clipboard
Paste	insert item contained in clipboard
Delete	remove selected item
Select All	choose all items

MacAPRS

You enter most MacAPRS commands by selecting a command from a pull-down menu or pull-down sub-menu, for example, to select the Edit - Clear Stations and Messages command, pull down the Edit menu and select Clear Stations and Messages. A few MacAPRS commands are selected by typing a control-character (e.g., [Home]).

Some MacAPRS commands have keyboard shortcuts, which are listed in brackets (e.g., [Cmd-O]) in the Menu Command column. You enter the shortcuts by holding down the Command [Cmd] key and pressing a second key, for example, to use the [Cmd-O] shortcut, you press the O key, while holding down the Cmd key.

Menu Command [Keyboard Shortcut]	Description
Apple > About MacAPRS	display information concerning MacAPRS
Apple > Bug Report	display form for reporting MacAPRS problems
File > New...	open new map window with default map
File > Open File... [Cmd-O]	load saved file into MacAPRS
File > Open Call Sign File...	load call sign directory file into MacAPRS
File > Close Window [Cmd-W]	close active open window
File > Save... [Cmd-S]	save displayed information as a file
File > Auto Save Map Window Image...	turn on/off automatic saving of active map
File > Save Window as HTML...	save displayed information in HTML format
File > Save Window Configuration...	create file containing current settings of windows
File > Simulate...	load file to simulate APRS activity
File > Get Map Info [Cmd-I]	display information regarding active map
File > Page Setup...	select printing parameters
File > Print... [Cmd-P]	print active open window
File > Merge Map Files...	combine maps to create new map

Command	Description
File > Quit [Cmd-Q]	quit MacAPRS
Edit > Cut [Cmd-X]	delete selected item and duplicate to clipboard
Edit > Copy [Cmd-C]	duplicate selected item to clipboard
Edit > Paste [Ctrl-V]	insert item contained in clipboard
Edit > Clear	delete selected item
Edit > Select All [Cmd-A]	choose all items in list
Edit > Find... [Cmd-F]	find station on map
Edit > Find Again... [Cmd-G]	repeat previous Edit > Find command
Edit > Calculate Distances... [Cmd-=]	determine distance and antenna bearing between received stations
Edit > Edit/Add Station/Object... [Cmd-E]	add or change station or object on map
Edit > Edit/Add Weather/Object...	add or change weather object on map
Edit > Edit/Add Waypoint...	add or change waypoint on map
Edit > Clear Stations	delete received station information
Edit > Clear Messages	delete received messages
Edit > Clear Wind Data	delete received wind data
Edit > Clear Region Search Index	delete contents of region search index
Settings > Master Mode > Normal Ham Operation	configure MacAPRS for normal APRS operation
Settings > Master Mode > Weather ONLY	configure MacAPRS for NWS/SKYWARN weather station operation
Settings > Master Mode > Space Mode	configure MacAPRS for MIR space station operation
Settings > Master Mode > Radio Dir Finding Extras	configure MacAPRS with additional direction finding features
Settings > General Display Settings...	configure miscellaneous map display options
Settings > Station Settings...	configure MacAPRS with station parameters

Command	Description
Settings > TNC Commands > Send RDF Report	transmit direction finding packet
Settings > TNC Commands > Send APRS Query [Cmd-/]	transmit APRS station query packet
Settings > TNC Commands > Send WX Query	transmit an APRS weather station query packet
Settings > TNC Commands > Send IGate Query	transmit APRS IGate station query packet
Settings > TNC Commands > VHF-Reinitialize TNC parameters	configure VHF/UHF TNC with TNC Settings parameters
Settings > TNC Commands > VHF-Exit KISS Mode	force VHF/UHF TNC to quit KISS mode
Settings > TNC Commands > VHF-Exit Kantronics Host Mode	force VHF/UHF TNC to quit Kantronics TNC host mode
Settings > TNC Commands > VHF-Exit AEA Host Mode	force VHF/UHF TNC to quit AEA TNC host mode
Settings > TNC Commands > HF-Reinitialize TNC	configure HF TNC with TNC Settings parameters
Settings > TNC Commands > HF-Exit KISS Mode	force HF TNC to quit KISS mode
Settings > TNC Commands > HF-Exit Kantronics Host Mode	force HF TNC to quit Kantronics TNC host mode
Settings > TNC Commands > HF-Exit AEA Host Mode	force HF TNC to quit AEA TNC host mode
Settings > Terminal Settings	configure settings for direct communications with TNC
Settings > Unproto APRSM Via (HF or Dual Port) > -None-	configure no Unproto HF path
Settings > Unproto APRSM Via (HF or Dual Port) > Default	configure Unproto HF path with default path
Settings > Unproto APRSM Via (HF or Dual Port) > Other...	configure Unproto HF path with user-defined path
Settings > Unproto APRSM Via (HF or Dual Port) > relay,WIDE	configure Unproto HF path as RELAY,WIDE
Settings > Unproto APRSM Via (HF or Dual Port) > WIDE,WIDE	configure Unproto HF path as WIDE,WIDE
Settings > Unproto APRSM Via (HF or Dual Port) > WIDE,GATE	configure Unproto HF path as WIDE,GATE
Settings > Unproto APRSM Via (HF or Dual Port) > WIDE-3	configure Unproto HF path as WIDE-3
Settings > Unproto APRSM Via (VHF) > -None-	configure no Unproto VHF/UHF path
Settings > Unproto APRSM Via (VHF) > Default	configure Unproto VHF/UHF path with default path

Command	Description
Settings > Unproto APRSM Via (VHF) > Other...	configure Unproto VHF/UHF path with user-defined path
Settings > Unproto APRSM Via (VHF) > relay,WIDE	configure Unproto VHF/UHF path as RELAY, WIDE
Settings > Unproto APRSM Via (VHF) > WIDE,WIDE	configure Unproto VHF/UHF path as WIDE,WIDE
Settings > Unproto APRSM Via (VHF) > WIDE,GATE	configure Unproto VHF/UHF path as WIDE,GATE
Settings > Unproto APRSM Via (VHF) > WIDE-3	configure Unproto VHF/UHF path as WIDE-3
Settings > Open HF TNC (Dual Port)	turn on/off communications with HF TNC
Settings > Open VHF TNC	turn on/off communications with VHF/UHF TNC
Settings > Open GPS/NMEA	turn on/off communications with NMEA/GPS equipment
Settings > Open Weather Station	turn on/off communications with weather station equipment
Settings > Open Direction Finding	turn on/off communications with direction finding equipment
Settings > Open Hard Copy Logging	turn on/off logging to printer
Settings > Open Echo Port	turn on/off echo port communications
Settings > Stop All Input	terminate all serial port communications
Settings > TCP/IP Connections > TCP/IP Settings	configure options regarding APRServer connections
Settings > TCP/IP Connections > Show TCP/IP Host List	display list of APRServers
Settings > TCP/IP Connections > Close All TCP ports	disconnect from all APRServer
Settings > TCP/IP Connections > Open Internet DGPS	connect to Differential GPS server
Settings > TCP/IP Connections > Connect To APRServe Network	connect to APRServer network
Settings > TCP/IP Connections > (server names)	connect to selected APRServer from list

Settings > Flag All Macs	log all stations using Macintosh OS to flagged station list
Settings > Flag All Windows	log all stations using Windows OS to flagged station list
Settings > GPS Alarm	configure options regarding GPS equipment alarms
Settings > Set Time from GPS	turn on/off determining MacAPRS time from GPS equipment
Settings > GPS Setup...	configure options regarding GPS equipment
Logging > Station Logging	turn on/off recording received station data
Logging > APRS Logging	turn on/off recording received APRS data
Logging > NMEA Logging	turn on/off recording received NMEA/GPS data
Logging > Local Weather Logging	turn on/off recording local weather reports
Logging > Message Logging	turn on/off recording received messages
Logging > Local RDF Logging	turn on/off recording local direction finding data
Logging > Statistics Logging	turn on/off recording received packet statistics
Logging > Stop All Logging	disable recording all received data
Maps > (map names)	display selected map from list
Display > Station Display Mode > Display All Stations	turn on/off display of all received stations on map
Display > Station Display Mode > Display Direct Stations Only	turn on/off display of directly received stations on map
Display > Station Display Mode > Display Flagged Stations Only	turn on/off display of only received flagged stations on map
Display > Station Display Mode > Display Tracked Stations Only	turn on/off display of only received tracked stations on map

Command	Description
Display > Station Display Mode > Display Weather Stations Only	turn on/off display of only received weather stations on map
Display > Station Display Mode > Station Display Mode...	configure options regarding display of stations on map
Display > Map Display Options	configure options regarding display of maps
Display > Home View (Home) [Cmd-H]	display current map in its default size
Display > Clear/Redraw [Cmd-L]	delete received data from map
Display > Center View	display center of map at mouse pointer location
Display > Zoom In 2X [Page Down]	magnify map by factor of 2
Display > Zoom In 4X	magnify map by factor of 4
Display > Zoom Out 2X [Page Up]	decrease map magnification by factor of 2
Display > Map Boundaries [Cmd-B]	display perimeters of available maps
Display > Overlays... > Display Overlay	display selected map overlay
Display > Overlays... > Display Overlay List	display list of map overlay components
Display > Overlays... > (overlay names)	select map overlay from list
Display > GridSquare (2 Ltr)	overlay 2-character Maidenhead grid squares on map
Display > GridSquare (4 Ltr)	overlay 4-character Maidenhead grid squares on map
Display > GridSquare (6 Ltr)	overlay 6-character Maidenhead grid squares on map
Display > Lat/Lon Lines	overlay latitude and longitude lines on map
Display > C.A.P. 15' Grids	overlay Civil Air Patrol grid squares on map
Display > Display Icons	turn on/off display of received station icons on map
Display > Display Call Signs	turn on/off display of received station call signs on map
Display > Display Labels	turn on/off display of labels on map
Display > Display Symbols	turn on/off display of symbols on map
Display > Display Filled Polygons	turn on/off display of filled polygons

Command	Description
Display > Display APRS Info (Bottom of Screen)	turn on/off display of most recently received APRS data at bottom of map
Display > Display NMEA Info (Bottom of Screen)	turn on/off display of most recently received NMEA data at bottom of map
Display > Display Course and Speed Vectors	turn on/off display of course and speed vectors of moving objects on map
Display > Display Dead Reckoning	turn on/off display of dead reckoning data
Display > Auto Scroll Moving Map	turn on/off automatic scrolling map function
Display > Display Airports	display location of airports on map
Display > Display Zip Codes	display location of ZIP Codes on map
Display > Display Coverage Circles [Cmd-D]	display circles representing received stations' coverage area
Display > Replay Selected Station [Cmd-R]	display course of selected tracked station on map
Display > Relay All Tracks	display course of all tracked station on map
Display > Display Balloon Prediction [Cmd-J]	display balloon prediction data
Display > Enable Deleted Stations	display previously deleted stations on map
Display > Delete Old Stations	delete old received stations from map
Lists > New Message... [Cmd-M]	compose and transmit new message or bulletin
Lists > Message List [Cmd-4]	display list of transmitted and received messages and bulletins
Lists > New NTS Message...	compose and transmit new National Traffic System message
Lists > NTS Message List	display list of transmitted and received National Traffic System messages

Lists > Map List	display list of available maps
Lists > Map Label List	display list of map labels
Lists > Station List [Cmd-1]	display list of received packet stations
Lists > Position List [Cmd-2]	display list of position information regarding received stations
Lists > When Heard	display list and graph of times that stations were received
Lists > Weather List [Cmd-3]	display list of received weather station data
Lists > Shelter List	display list of received emergency shelter object data
Lists > Hurricane List	display list of received hurricane object data
Lists > Flagged Station List	display list of received flagged stations
Lists > Track List	display list of received tracked station data
Lists > TCP/IP List	display list of data concerning stations received via the APRServer
Lists > Mic Enc List	display list of received MIC Encoder station data
Lists > RDF List	display list of received direction finding station data
Lists > ProtoPath List	display list of received stations' Unproto paths
Lists > History List [Cmd-5]	display list of all received packets
Lists > CallBook List [Cmd-0]	display list of CD-ROM call sign directory entries
Lists > APRS Statistics [Cmd-6]	display graphic representing APRS activity for previous day, week, year
Lists > Weather Display [Cmd-8]	display graphic representing local weather station equipment
Lists > 24 Hr Weather Charts [Cmd-7]	display graphic representing local weather data for previous 24 hours

Command	Description
Lists > NWS-Counties list	display list of counties with National Weather System alarms
Lists > NMEA Display [Cmd-9]	display GPS receiver heads up window
Lists > Altitude Statistics	display chart representing altitude statistics
Lists > Wind Interpolation	display graphic representing wind interpolation
Lists > Icon List	display list of MacAPRS icons
Lists > Global Label List	display list of global labels
Lists > Airport List	display list of airports
Lists > Internal State	display various MacAPRS parameters
Lists > Packet Statistics	display statistics regarding received packet activity
Lists > DX Countries List	display list of received DX stations
Lists > IOTA List	display list of received islands
Lists > Way Point List	display list of received waypoints
Lists > IGate Stations List	display list of received IGate stations
Windows > Next Window [Cmd-']	deselect active window and select an inactive window
Windows > New Map Window Square [Cmd-N]	open new map window with default map
Windows > New Map Window Polar	open new map window with default map in polar projection
Windows > New Map Window DEM	open new map window with selected Digital Elevation Model map
Windows > New Map Window DEM > About DEM	display help for Digital Elevation Model maps
Windows > New Map Window DEM > (map names)	display selected Digital Elevation Model map from list
Windows > New Map Window Tiger	display map received via Internet from Tiger server
Windows > New Map Window Intellicast > About Intellicast	display help for Intellicast weather maps

Command	Description
Windows > New Map Window Intellicast > Intellicast Composit	display composite weather map received via Internet from Intellicast
Windows > New Map Window Intellicast > (map names)	display selected weather map received via Internet from Intellicast server from list
Windows > Close All Windows	close all open windows
Windows > Stack All Windows	resize and arrange open windows in a
Windows > Tile Windows	resize and arrange open windows side-by-side
Windows > Reset Window Locations	resize and arrange open windows in a stack
Windows > Terminal Window	open window for direct communications with TNC
Windows > Garmin GPS Window	open window for controlling Garmin GPS receivers
Windows > ICONs	display all MacAPRS icons
Windows > TCP Connection Status	display information concerning connection to APRServer
Windows > (window names)	display selected map from list

pocketAPRS

You choose most pocketAPRS commands by tapping the Menu button, then selecting a command from a pull-down menu, for example, to select the Menu > Settings > Filters command, you tap the MENU button, tap the Settings menu and tap Filters. You choose immediate transmit commands by tapping the beach ball icon, then tapping the desired immediate transmit command. In the Map, Message, Station List, and Status List windows, you select a list command by tapping the down arrow (t), then tapping the desired list command.

Some pocketAPRS commands have shortcuts, which are listed in brackets (e.g., [/S]) in the Menu Command column. You enter the shortcuts in the Palm III Graffiti window by entering the command stroke and the applicable shortcut character, for example, to use the [/S] shortcut, enter the command stroke [/] and the letter S.

Menu Command [Keyboard Shortcut]	Description
Menu > Main > About pocketAPRS	display information concerning pocketAPRS
Menu > Main > pocketAPRS Help [/H]	display help for pocketAPRS
Menu > Main > Add Object [/A]	add, change, or delete an APRS object
Menu > Main > Send Message [/S]	compose and transmit message, bulletin, or announcement
Menu > Main > Manual DF Report [/D]	enter compass bearing for direction finding
Menu > Main > Edit Map List	delete map(s) from pocketAPRS
Menu > Main > Quit	quit pocketAPRS
Menu > Views > Map [/M]	display selected map
Menu > Views > Station List [/P]	display list of received stations
Menu > Views > Status List [/L]	display list of received station status information
Menu > Views > Messages [/M]	display list of received messages, bulletins, etc.
Menu > Views > View Packets [/V]	display list of received packets
Menu > Settings > pocketAPRS Settings	configure pocketAPRS parameters

Command	
Menu > Settings > Station Settings	configure station parameters
Menu > Settings > Filters	configure packet filtering
Menu > Settings > Transmit Control	configure packet transmission parameters
Menu > Settings > RDF Control	configure direction finding equipment parameters
Menu > Settings > Alarms & Alerts	configure APRS, digipeater, and GPS alerts and alarms
Menu > Settings > Map Display	configure map display options
Menu > Settings > Object Display	configure object display options
(Beach Ball Icon) > Transmit Position	send position packet
(Beach Ball Icon) > Transmit Status	send status packet
(Beach Ball Icon) > Transmit Objects	send APRS object packet
(Beach Ball Icon) > Transmit Messages	send message, bulletin, announcement, etc.
(Beach Ball Icon) > Transmit All	send all
(Beach Ball Icon) > APRS Query All	send APRS query packet
(Beach Ball Icon) > APRS Query Local	send APRS query packet to nearby stations
(Beach Ball Icon) > Reintialize TNC	configure TNC with selected Settings menus parameters

Map Window Menu Command — **Description**

t > 1/64 X to 64 X	increase/decrease map magnification by selected factor
(Map Icon) > (map names)	display selected map from list

Messages List Window Menu Command — **Description**

t > All	display all messages and bulletins
t > Normal	display all messages only
t > Bulletins	display all bulletins only

t > Announcements   display all announcements only

t > Weather   display all weather messages only

t > Special Bulletins   display all special bulletins only

Station List/Status List Window Menu Command Description

t > Status   display list of status information regarding received stations

t > Position   display list of position information regarding received stations

t > Data   display list of station data regarding received stations

t > Distance   display list of distances between you and the received stations

t > Heard   display list of received stations in the order they were received

t > Digi Path   display list of Unprotocol path of received stations

t > Alerts   display list of alerts from received stations

TH-D7

You access menu selections in the Kenwood TH-D7 APRS Mode by pressing the MENU key, then either use the number keys to select the desired menu numbers or use the cursor keys to scroll to the desired menu number. Press the OK key to confirm a menu selection and press the MENU key to exit the menu mode.

Menu Command	Description
MENU-2-1	enter call sign and SSID
MENU-2-2	turn on/off operation with GPS receiver
MENU-2-3	enter station latitude and longitude
MENU-2-4	select MIC Encoder comment
MENU-2-5	select station icon
MENU-2-6	enter APRS status text

MENU-2-7	select beacon timing
MENU-2-8	enter Unprotocol path
MENU-2-9	select beacon transmission method
MENU-2-A	configure packet group code filtering
MENU-2-B	configure packet distance filtering
MENU-2-C	select units of measurement for distance and temperature

WinAPRS

You choose most Display > Direct Stations Only command, you pull down the Display menu and select Direct Stations Only. A few WinAPRS commands are entered by typing a control-character (e.g., [Home]), or pressing a function-key (e.g., [F5]).

Some WinAPRS commands have keyboard shortcuts which are listed in brackets (e.g., [B]) in the Menu Command column. You enter most WinAPRS shortcuts by simply typing the shortcut key, for example, to use the [B] shortcut, you type B.

Menu Command [Keyboard Shortcut]	Description
File > About WinAPRS	display information concerning WinAPRS
File > Open	load saved file into WinAPRS
File > Save [Ctrl-S]	save displayed information as a file
File > Save Window Config	create file containing current settings of windows
File > Close [Ctrl-W]	close active open window
File > Demo Mode	load file to demonstrate WinAPRS
File > Simulate...	load file to simulate APRS activity
File > Simulate Live GPS...	load file to simulate GPS activity

File > Print	print active open window
File > Exit	quit WinAPRS
Edit > Copy [Ctrl-C]	duplicate selected item to clipboard
Edit > Select All [Ctrl-A]	choose all items
Edit > Find [Ctrl-F]	find station on map
Edit > Find Again [Ctrl-G]	repeat previous Edit > Find command
Edit > Edit/Add Station/Object...	add or change station or object on map
Edit > Edit/Add Weather/Object...	add or change weather object on map
Edit > Clear Stations	delete received station information
Edit > Clear Messages	delete received messages
Settings > Master Mode > Normal Ham Operation	configure WinAPRS for normal APRS operation
Settings > Master Mode > Weather Only	configure WinAPRS for NWS/SKYWARN weather station operation
Settings > Master Mode > Space Mode	configure WinAPRS for MIR space station operation
Settings > Master Mode > Radio Dir Finding Extras	configure WinAPRS with additional direction finding features
Settings > General Display	configure miscellaneous map display options
Settings > Station	configure WinAPRS with station parameters
Settings > WinAPRS	configure WinAPRS with APRS parameters
Settings > Serial Port	configure serial port
Settings > Select TNC Type	choose type of TNC used with WinAPRS
Settings > TNC	configure WinAPRS with TNC parameters
Settings > Position Report Rate	configure rate of position packet transmissions
Settings > Weather	configure WinAPRS with weather station equipment parameters
Settings > CallBook DataBase	configure CD-ROM call sign directory

Command	Description
Settings > Enable Sound	configure WinAPRS sound options
Settings > Open VHF TNC	turn on/off communications with VHF/UHF TNC
Settings > Open HF TNC (Dual)	turn on/off communications with HF TNC
Settings > Open WX Port	turn on/off communications with weather station equipment
Settings > Open GPS Port	turn on/off communications with NMEA/GPS equipment
Settings > Open RDF Port	turn on/off communications with direction finding equipment
Settings > Close TNC	disable communications with TNC
Settings > Close All Ports	disable communications with all external equipment
Settings > KISS Mode Options	configure options for KISS mode
Settings > TNC Commands > Send Position [F2]	transmit position packet
Settings > TNC Commands > Send Objects	transmit objects packet
Settings > TNC Commands > Send Grid-Square Position	transmit Maidenhead grid square packet
Settings > TNC Commands > Send Weather Report	transmit weather report packet
Settings > TNC Commands > Send RDF Report	transmit direction finding packet
Settings > TNC Commands > Send APRS Query	transmit APRS station query packet
Settings > TNC Commands > Send WX Query	transmit an APRS weather station query packet
Settings > TNC Commands > Send IGate Query	transmit APRS IGate station query packet
Settings > TNC Commands > VHF-Reinitialize TNC	configure VHF/UHF TNC with TNC Settings parameters
Settings > TNC Commands > VHF-Exit KISS Mode	force VHF/UHF TNC to quit KISS mode
Settings > TNC Commands > VHF-Exit Kantronics Host Mode	force VHF/UHF TNC to quit Kantronics TNC host mode
Settings > TNC Commands > VHF-Exit AEA Host Mode	force VHF/UHF TNC to quit AEA TNC host mode
Settings > TNC Commands > HF-Reinitialize TNC	configure HF TNC with TNC Settings parameters
Settings > TNC Commands > HF-Exit KISS Mode	force HF TNC to quit KISS mode

Command	Description
Settings > TNC Commands > TCP/IP Connections > Connect To APRServe Network	connect to APRServer network
Settings > TNC Commands > TCP/IP Connections > (server names)	connect to selected APRServer from list
Settings > TNC Commands > Send Position [F2]	transmit position packet
Settings > TNC Commands > Send Query	transmit APRS query packet
Settings > TNC Commands > Send Weather	transmit weather report packet
Settings > TNC Commands > Send WX Query	transmit an APRS weather station query packet
Logging > Station Logging	turn on/off recording received station data
Logging > WinAPRS Logging	turn on/off recording received APRS data
Logging > NMEA Logging	turn on/off recording received NMEA/GPS data
Logging > Local Weather Logging	turn on/off recording local weather reports
Logging > Message Logging	turn on/off recording received messages
Logging > Local RDF Logging	turn on/off recording local direction finding data
Logging > Stop All Logging	disable recording all received data
Maps > Display Map Boundaries [B]	display perimeters of available maps
Maps > Map List Window	display all selectable maps
Maps > (map names)	display selected map from list
Display > Home View [H]	display current map in its default size
Display > Auto Refresh Maps	turn on/off automatic map refreshing function
Display > Auto Scroll Moving Maps	turn on/off automatic scrolling map function
Display > Station Call Signs	turn on/off display of received station call signs on map
Display > Station Icons	turn on/off display of received station icons on map

Display > Map Labels	turn on/off display of labels on map
Display > Map Symbols	turn on/off display of symbols on map
Display > Filled Polygons	turn on/off display of filled polygons
Display > Course and Speed	turn on/off display of course and speed vectors of moving objects on map
Display > Dead Reckoning	turn on/off display of dead reckoning data
Display > All Stations	turn on/off display of all received stations on map
Display > Direct Stations Only	turn on/off display of directly received stations on map
Display > Flagged Stations Only	turn on/off display of only received flagged stations on map
Display > Tracked Stations Only	turn on/off display of only received tracked stations on map
Display > Weather Stations Only	turn on/off display of only received weather stations on map
Display > Station Display Options	configure options regarding display of stations on map
Display > Map Display Options	configure options regarding display of maps
Display > Overlays > Display Overlay [O]	display selected map overlay
Display > Overlays > Display Overlay List	display list of map overlay components
Display > Overlays > (overlay names)	select map overlay from list
Display > GridSquare (2 Ltr) [G]	overlay 2-character Maidenhead grid squares on map
Display > GridSquare (4 Ltr)	overlay 4-character Maidenhead grid squares on map
Display > GridSquare (6 Ltr)	overlay 6-character Maidenhead grid squares on map
Display > Civil Air Patrol Grids [C]	overlay Civil Air Patrol grid squares on map
Display > Airports	display location of airports on map
Display > Coverage Circles	display circles representing received stations' coverage area
Display > Zipcodes	display location of ZIP Codes on map
Display > Replay Track	display course of selected tracked station on map

Command	Description
Display > Relay All Tracks	display course of all tracked station on map
Lists > New Message [F7]	compose and transmit new message or bulletin
Lists > Message List	display list of transmitted and received messages and bulletins
Lists > New NTS Message	compose and transmit new National Traffic System message
Lists > NTS Message List	display list of transmitted and received National Traffic System messages
Lists > Map List	display list of available maps
Lists > Map Label List	display list of map labels
Lists > Station List	display list of received packet stations
Lists > Position List	display list of position information regarding received stations
Lists > When Heard	display list and graph of times that stations were received
Lists > Weather List	display list of received weather station data
Lists > Shelter List	display list of received emergency shelter object data
Lists > Hurricane List	display list of received hurricane object data
Lists > Flagged Station List	display list of received flagged stations
Lists > Track List	display list of received tracked station data
Lists > Mic Enc List	display list of received MIC Encoder station data
Lists > RDF List	display list of received direction finding station data
Lists > TCP/IP List	display list of data concerning stations received via the APRServer network
Lists > ProtoPath List	display list of received stations' Unproto paths
Lists > History List	display list of all received packets
Lists > CallBook List	display list of CD-ROM call sign directory entries
Lists > Icon List	display list of WinAPRS icons

Command	Description
Lists > Global Label List	display list of global labels
Lists > Airport List	display list of airports
Lists > Internal State	display various WinAPRS parameters
Lists > Packet Statistics	display statistics regarding received packet activity
Lists > APRS Statistics	display graphic representing APRS activity for previous day, week, year
Lists > Weather Display	display graphic representing local weather station equipment
Lists > 24 Hr Weather Chart	display graphic representing local weather data for previous 24 hours
Lists > NWS-Counties List	display list of counties with National Weather System alarms
Lists > NMEA Display	display GPS receiver heads up window
Lists > Waypoint List	display list of received waypoints
Lists > DXCC List	display list of received DX stations
Lists > IGate List	display list of received IGate stations
Windows > Next Window [F6]	deselect active window and select an inactive window
Windows > New Map Square	open new map window with default map
Windows > New Map Polar	open new map window with default map in polar projection
Windows > Image Files > About DEMs	display help for Digital Elevation Model maps
Windows > Image Files > About Image	display help for Digital Elevation Model maps
Windows > Image Files > (image names)	display selected Digital Elevation Model map from list
Windows > New Map Prec Mapping	display Precision Mapping Street software map
Windows > New Map Tiger	display map received via Internet from Tiger server
Windows > Intellicast Weather Maps > About Intellicast	display help for Intellicast weather maps

Windows > Intellicast Weather Maps > Composite Intellicast Map	display composite weather map received via Internet from Intellicast server
Windows > Intellicast Weather Maps > (map names)	display selected weather map received via Internet from Intellicast server from list
Windows > Cascade	resize and arrange open windows in a stack
Windows > Tile	resize and arrange open windows side-by-side
Windows > Reset Window Locations	resize and arrange open windows in a stack
Windows > Arrange Icons	arrange map icons
Windows > Terminal Window	open window for direct communications with TNC
Windows > Garmin GPS Window	open window for controlling Garmin GPS receivers
Windows > ICON Window	display all WinAPRS icons
Windows > TCP Connection Status	display information concerning connection to APRServer
Windows > (window names)	display selected window from list
Help > Help Window [F1]	display help for WinAPRS
Help > Bug Report Form	display form for reporting WinAPRS problems
Help > About WinAPRS	display information concerning WinAPRS

APPENDIX C

GLOSSARY

American National Standard Code for Information Interchange (ASCII)—a seven bit digital code used in computer and radioteleprinter applications.

AO16APRS—an email list sponsored by TAPR that is devoted to the discussion of using APRS with Amateur Radio satellites.

APRS—abbreviation for Automatic Position Reporting System.

APRS (DOS)—the original version of APRS; it runs on a *DOS* platform.

APRS/CE—a version of APRS that runs on *Windows CE* platforms.

APRS+SA—a version of APRS that runs on a *Windows* platform using maps running concurrently on DeLorme Street Atlas software.

APRServer—an Internet site that collects APRS data from IGates to permit the viewing of worldwide APRS activity via the Internet.

APRSFD—an email list sponsored by TAPR that is intended for the discussion of using APRS in conjunction with Field Day operations.

APRSNEWS—an email list sponsored by TAPR that provides for the distribution of APRS news concerning new releases of software.

APRSSIG—an email list sponsored by TAPR that is intended for the discussion of all APRS topics.

APRSSPEC—an email list sponsored by TAPR that is intended for the discussion of the APRS protocol documentation project.

ASCII—abbreviation for American National Standard Code for Information Interchange.

asynchronous—a data transmission timing technique that adds extra bits of information to indicate the beginning and end of each transmitted character.

audio-frequency-shift keying (AFSK)—a method of transmitting digital information by switching between two audio tones fed into the transmitter audio input.

Automatic Position Reporting System (APRS)—a packet radio application for tracking real-time events by graphically displaying information on maps displayed on the user's computer screen.

baud—a unit of signaling speed equal to one pulse (event or symbol) per second in a single-channel transmission.

beacon—a TNC function that permits a station to automatically send unconnected packets at regular intervals.

bit—binary digit, a signal that is either on/one or off/zero; bits are combined to represent alphanumeric and control characters for data communications.

BText—the TNC command that configures the contents of a packet radio beacon.

byte—a group of bits, usually eight in number.

CGA—abbreviation for color graphics adapter.

Clear To Send (CTS)—an EIA-232 serial interface signal, which informs the DTE when the DCE is ready to transmit data.

color graphics adapter (CGA)—a computer monitor type or standard.

CTS—abbreviation for Clear To Send.

data circuit-terminating equipment, data communications equipment (DCE)—the device that provides communications between a DTE and radio equipment or telephone lines.

data terminal equipment (DTE)—a device that is used as an interface between a human and a computer to allow the human to exchange information with the computer.

Data Terminal Ready (DTR)—an EIA-232 serial interface signal, which informs the DCE when the DTE is ready for data communications.

DB-25—a connector that transfers 25 signals, typically used for computer serial port connections.

DB-9—a connector that transfers 9 signals, typically used for computer serial port connections.

DCE—abbreviation for data circuit-terminating equipment and data communications equipment.

default—the state of computer software or computer hardware after the computer ware is initially turned on or reset.

deviation—in the FM mode, the amount that the carrier frequency is shifted in proportion to the amplitude of the input signal.

DF—abbreviation for direction finding.

digipeater—digital repeater, a device that receives, temporarily stores and then transmits (repeats) packet radio transmissions that are specifically addressed for routing through the digipeater.

direction finding (DF)—a means of locating a radio station by determining the compass bearing of the source of the radio station's signal.

Doppler—the change of frequency of a radio wave that occurs as the velocity of its source changes relative to the observer.

DTE—abbreviation for data terminal equipment.

DTR—abbreviation for Data Terminal Ready.

EGA—abbreviation for enhanced graphics adapter.

EIA—abbreviation for Electronic Industries Association.

EIA-232—the EIA standard for DTE-to-DCE (TNC) interfacing that specifies the interface signals and their electrical characteristics.

EIA-422—an EIA standard for DTE-to-DCE (TNC) interfacing that specifies the interface signals and their electrical characteristics.

Electronic Industries Association (EIA)—an organization composed of representatives of the United States electronics industry; the EIA is involved in formulating data communication standards.

enhanced graphics adapter (EGA)—a computer monitor type or standard.

Enter—a key on a computer keyboard that causes the computer to accept the information previously typed at its keyboard.

enter—to use a key (for example, the Enter key) on a computer keyboard to cause the computer to accept the information previously typed at its keyboard.

fade point—the location where a direction-finding station loses or acquires the signal transmitted by an unknown radio station.

gateway—a device that allows packet radio stations on different operating frequencies to communicate with each other.

Global Positioning System (GPS)—a system that uses orbiting satellites to determine the location of GPS receiving stations on the surface of the Earth.

GPS—abbreviation for Global Positioning System.

HAAT—abbreviation for Height Above Average Terrain.

Hardware Single Port Switch (HSP)—a circuit built into a cable that permits the connection of a GPS receiver and a TNC to the same computer serial port.

Height Above Average Terrain (HAAT)—the difference between the elevation of an antenna and the average elevation of the land area surrounding the antenna.

HotSync—the process of transferring data between a Palm III PDA and a computer.

HSP—abbreviation for Hardware Single Port Switch.

HTAPRS—an email list sponsored by TAPR that is devoted to the discussion of APRS topics related to the Kenwood TH-D7 handheld transceiver.

IGate—an APRS station connected to the Internet that relays the APRS data it receives locally to central Internet sites called APRServers.

kbyte—one thousand bytes.

Long Range Navigation (LORAN)—a radio system used by ships and planes to determine their location.

LORAN—abbreviation for Long Range Navigation.

MacAPRS—a version of APRS that runs on a Macintosh platform.

MIC—abbreviation for microphone.

MIC-E—an email list sponsored by TAPR that is intended for the discussion of the MIC-E module.

Micro Interface Module (MIM)—a telemetry TNC in one integrated circuit.

MIM—abbreviation for Micro Interface Module.

modem—modulator-demodulator; an electronic device that permits digital equipment to use analog communications media for data communications.

MYAlias—the TNC command that configures a pseudonym for the identification of a packet radio station.

MYCall—the TNC command that configures the identification of a packet radio station.

National Marine Electronics Association (NMEA)—the organization responsible for the standards used for GPS and other navigation systems.

network—a system of interconnected packet radio stations assembled for the efficient transfer of packets over long distances.

NMEA—abbreviation for National Marine Electronics Association.

NMEA-0183—a standard used for GPS and other navigation systems, which was developed by the National Marine Electronics Association (NMEA); it is compatible with APRS.

path—the route between two connected packet radio stations consisting of digipeaters and other packet stations.

PDA—abbreviation for personal digital assistant.

PHGD—abbreviation for Power-Height-Gain-Direction.

pocketAPRS—a version of APRS that runs on the 3Com Palm III Connected Organizer, a hand-held personal digital assistant (PDA).

port—a circuit that allows a device to communicate with external devices.

posit text—a short string of text sent whenever APRS transmits a station's position packet.

position comment—a short string of text sent whenever APRS transmits a station's position packet.

position packet—an Unnumbered Information (UI) packet generated by APRS that contains information concerning the location of the APRS station; the latitude and longitude of an APRS station.

Power-Height-Gain-Direction (PHGD)—information concerning an APRS station that may be included in its APRS transmissions.

PROPNET—an email list sponsored by TAPR that is devoted to an ongoing VHF propagation experiment using APRS.

PTT—abbreviation for press-to-talk.

radio port—the TNC port that is connected to a radio transceiver (or transmitter and receiver)

RAM—abbreviation for random-access memory.

random-access memory (RAM)—a data storage device that can be written to and read from.

Received Data—an EIA-232 serial interface signal that consists of data from the DCE (TNC) that was received over the communication medium and demodulated by the DCE (TNC).

RELAY—an APRS digipeater that has a small coverage area; it is intended to feed its packets to WIDE digipeaters that have coverage of wide expanses of an APRS network.

RJ-45—a connector that transfers 6 signals, typically used for computer serial port connections.

Secondary Station Identifier (SSID)—a number that follows a packet radio station call sign to differentiate between two or more packet radio stations operating under the same call sign.

serial port—an interconnection that transfers bit-encoded information bit-by-bit (serially); the TNC connection for a terminal or computer.

Signal Ground—an EIA-232 serial interface signal that provides a common ground reference for all the other interface signals except Shield (pin 1).

SSID—abbreviation for secondary station identifier.

status text—a short string of text sent whenever APRS transmits a station's beacon.

stop bit—one or two extra bits that follow a character to indicate its end in asynchronous data communications.

TAPR—abbreviation for Tucson Amateur Packet Radio Corporation.

telemetry—information collected remotely that is transmitted to a distant collection site.

terminal—short for data terminal equipment or a computer emulating data terminal equipment.

terminal node controller (TNC)—an Amateur Radio packet assembler/disassembler; may or may not include a modem.

TNC—abbreviation for terminal-node controller.

TNC 2—the second generation TAPR TNC that was based on a Z80 microprocessor; its design was the most popular in amateur packet radio history.

TRACEn-n—an APRS digipeater protocol that simplifies digipeater addressing and permits tracking the digipeater path of a packet.

Transmitted Data—an EIA-232 serial interface signal that consists of data from a DTE that is intended for transmission by the DCE (TNC) over the communication medium; also called Send Data.

Tucson Amateur Packet Radio Corporation (TAPR)—the Amateur Radio organization that is instrumental in packet radio protocol and hardware developments in the United States.

TXdelay—the TNC command that configures the length of time inserted between the time the TNC keys a transmitter and the time the TNC sends data to the transmitter.

UI—abbreviation for Unnumbered Information frame.

unconnected packets—packets transmitted from a source station with no specific destination station being addressed.

United States Geological Survey (USGS)—a federal agency which is a source for map data used for creating APRS maps.

Universal Serial Bus (USB)—a standard for interfacing computer devices.

Unnumbered Information (UI)—an AX.25 unnumbered frame that allows data to be transmitted from a source station with no specific destination station being addressed.

Unproto—the TNC command that determines the digipeater path of packets sent in the unconnected (unprotocol) mode.

Unprotocol—the packet radio mode in which packets are broadcasted, rather than being transmitted to a specifically addressed connected station.

USB—abbreviation for Universal Serial Bus.

USGS—abbreviation for United States Geological Survey.

VGA—abbreviation for video graphics adapter.

video graphics adapter (VGA)—a computer monitor type or standard.

WIDE—an APRS digipeater that is well-situated in order to provide coverage of wide expanses of an APRS network.

WIDEn-n—an APRS digipeater protocol that simplifies digipeater addressing and promotes network efficiency.

WinAPRS—a version of APRS that runs on a *Windows* platform.

XAPRS—a version of APRS that runs on *Linux* platforms.

XASTIR—a version of APRS that runs on *Linux* platforms.

XOFF—transmitter off; a flow control character used in ASCII data transfers; it commands the transmitter to stop sending data.

XON—transmitter on; a flow control character used in ASCII data transfers; it commands the transmitter to send data.

ABOUT THE ARRL

The seed for Amateur Radio was planted in the 1890s, when Guglielmo Marconi began his experiments in wireless telegraphy. Soon he was joined by dozens, then hundreds, of others who were enthusiastic about sending and receiving messages through the air—some with a commercial interest, but others solely out of a love for this new communications medium. The United States government began licensing Amateur Radio operators in 1912.

By 1914, there were thousands of Amateur Radio operators—hams—in the United States. Hiram Percy Maxim, a leading Hartford, Connecticut, inventor and industrialist saw the need for an organization to band together this fledgling group of radio experimenters. In May 1914 he founded the American Radio Relay League (ARRL) to meet that need.

Today ARRL, with approximately 170,000 members, is the largest organization of radio amateurs in the United States. The ARRL is a not-for-profit organization that:

- promotes interest in Amateur Radio communications and experimentation
- represents US radio amateurs in legislative matters, and
- maintains fraternalism and a high standard of conduct among Amateur Radio operators.

At ARRL headquarters in the Hartford suburb of Newington, the staff helps serve the needs of members. ARRL is also International Secretariat for the International Amateur Radio Union, which is made up of similar societies in 150 countries around the world.

ARRL publishes the monthly journal *QST*, as well as newsletters and many publications covering all aspects of Amateur Radio. Its headquarters station, W1AW, transmits Morse code practice sessions and bulletins of interest to radio amateurs. The ARRL also coordinates an extensive field organization, which includes volunteers who provide technical information and other support for radio amateurs as well as communications for public-service activities. In addition, ARRL represents US amateurs with the Federal Communications Commission and other government agencies in the US and abroad.

Membership in ARRL means much more than receiving *QST* each month. In addition to the services already described, ARRL offers membership services on a personal level, such as the ARRL Volunteer Examiner Coordinator Program and a QSL bureau.

Full ARRL membership (available only to licensed radio amateurs in the US) gives you a voice in how the affairs of the organization are governed. ARRL policy is set by a Board of Directors (one from each of 15 Divisions). Each year, one-third of the ARRL Board of Directors stands for election by the Full Members they represent. The day-to-day operation of ARRL HQ is managed by an Executive Vice President and a Chief Financial Officer.

No matter what aspect of Amateur Radio attracts you, ARRL membership is relevant and important. There would be no Amateur Radio as we know it today were it not for the ARRL. We would be happy to welcome you as a member! (An Amateur Radio license is not required for Associate Membership.) For more information about ARRL and answers to any questions you may have about Amateur Radio, write or call:

ARRL—the national association for Amateur Radio
225 Main Street
Newington CT 06111-1494
(860) 594-0200
Prospective new amateurs call:
800-32-NEW HAM (800-326-3942)
E-mail: **newham@arrl.org**
World Wide Web: **http://www.arrl.org/**

INDEX

222

FEEDBACK

Please use this form to give us your comments on this book and what you'd like to see in future editions. You can also e-mail your comments to us at **pubsfdbk@arrl.org** (publications feedback). In that case, please be sure to include your name, call, e-mail address and the book title and edition in the body of your e-mail message. Also indicate whether or not you are an ARRL member.

Where did you purchase this book?
    ☐ From ARRL directly   ☐ From an ARRL dealer

Is there a dealer who carries ARRL publications within:
    ☐ 5 miles   ☐ 15 miles   ☐ 30 miles of your location?   ☐ Not sure.

License class:
☐ Novice	☐ Technician	☐ Technician Plus
☐ General	☐ Advanced	☐ Extra

Name _____

ARRL member? ☐ Yes ☐ No

Call Sign _____

Daytime Phone ( ) _____

Age _____

Address _____

E-mail address _____

City, State/Province, ZIP/Postal Code _____

If licensed, how long? _____

Other hobbies _____

Occupation _____

For ARRL use only	APRS-2
Edition	1 2 3 4 5 6 7 8 9 10 11 12
Printing	1 2 3 4 5 6 7 8 9 10 11 12

From _____

_____

_____

EDITOR, APRS-2
ARRL
225 MAIN STREET
NEWINGTON CT 06111-1494

.... please fold and tape ....